WITHDRAWN

D1266193

THE COMMONWEALTH AND INTERNATIONAL LIBRARY
Joint Chairmen of the Honorary Editorial Advisory Board
SIR ROBERT ROBINSON, O.M., F.R.S., LONDON
DEAN ATHELSTAN SPILHAUS, MINNESOTA
Publisher: ROBERT MAXWELL, M.C., M.P.

SELECTED READINGS IN PHYSICS
General Editor: D. TER HAAR

Wave Mechanics

Wave Mechanics

by GUNTER LUDWIG

THE QUEEN'S AWARD TO INDUSTRY 1966

PERGAMON PRESS

OXFORD · LONDON · EDINBURGH · NEW YORK
TORONTO · SYDNEY · PARIS · BRAUNSCHWEIG

Pergamon Press Ltd., Headington Hill Hall, Oxford
4 & 5 Fitzroy Square, London W.1

Pergamon Press (Scotland) Ltd., 2 & 3 Teviot Place, Edinburgh 1

Pergamon Press Inc., 44–01 21st Street, Long Island City, New York 11101

Pergamon of Canada, Ltd., 6 Adelaide Street East, Toronto, Ontario

Pergamon Press (Aust.) Pty. Ltd., Rushcutters Bay,
Sydney, New South Wales

Pergamon Press S.A.R.L., 24 rue des Écoles, Paris 5e

Vieweg & Sohn GmbH, Burgplatz 1, Braunschweig

Copyright © 1968 Pergamon Press Ltd.

First edition 1968

Library of Congress Catalog Card No. 66-30631

QC
174.2
L8
1968

This book is sold subject to the condition
that it shall not, by way of trade, be lent,
resold, hired out, or otherwise disposed
of without the publisher's consent,
in any form of binding or cover
other than that in which
it is published

08 103204 8 (Flexicover)
08 203204 1 (hard cover)

WHEATON COLLEGE LIBRARY
NORTON, MASS.

145814

Contents

PART 1

CHAPTER I

Historical Development and Deductive Construction of a Theory

IN ACCORDANCE with the idea of this series, this book is not intended to give a systematic or textbook account of quantum theory. On the contrary, it will sketch, on the basis of the originals reprinted in Part 2, how the discovery of quantum theory was arrived at. It might be asked in what way this can be of interest to us today.

When a complete theory is described in lectures, textbooks or monographs, frequently only the content of this theory is given in as clear a form as possible. In these circumstances, the question generally remains open as to how this theory was arrived at. Without taking account of its historical development, an existing theory often appears almost as if it had "fallen from heaven". However, the question of the development of a theory is important not only to satisfy our curiosity but also because much can be learnt from it for the future. For while it is possible to learn the content of a theory systematically, there is no method that can be learnt for finding new theories. Since (probably as a basic principle) there can be no such method, we are thrown back to the study of the development of known theories in order to awaken our capacity for tracing physical relationships and, which may often be decisive, eliminating inhibitions and prejudices with respect to the method of a new theory and the aim that it is to achieve.

Before we turn with this purpose to the discovery of quantum mechanics in the papers of Heisenberg, Born, and Jordan on the one hand and de Broglie and Schrödinger on the other hand, we must give a brief account of what we understand by a theory for a certain physical field. Summarizing the matter in one sentence we may say: a physical theory is a mathematical picture of a section of reality.

From this it follows that a theory has three essential parts:

(1) A mathematical system, i.e. a range of mathematical objects with abstractly defined relations and structures. For example, we may think of Maxwell's equations for the quantities $\boldsymbol{E}$, $\boldsymbol{B}$, ϱ, $\boldsymbol{j}$, without thereby taking their physical significance into consideration.

(2) A domain of determinable facts; in the case of modern physics such a field scarcely belongs to everyday experience (even partially), since only very complicated experiments yield the desired objectively determinable effects. We shall call this field briefly the physical field of the theory.

(3) A system of prescriptions correlating mathematical quantities and physical facts, i.e. experimentally obtained results.

There is a noteworthy difference between (1) and (2) which must therefore also be expressed in (3): while a mathematical system is always an exact and well-defined system (otherwise it would not be a mathematical system at all), all ideas about facts have a significance which is not quite sharply delimited, an inherent range of uncertainty (very frequently dependent on the particular experimental situation concerned). By this range of uncertainty we do not mean any inaccuracies of measurement (since to be able to speak meaningfully of these inaccuracies of measurement the magnitude to be measured must be "defined" more accurately than the apparatus concerned measures it) nor any statistical frequency resulting not from the measuring apparatus but from the totality of objects to be measured. What we mean here by the range of uncertainty is in fact the range of uncertainty of the definition of a physical quantity itself. Let us, for example, think of the definition of a length. Physically, the length is defined by prescriptions of measurement and is therefore defined just to the extent that these prescriptions of measurement prove to be capable of being carried out, i.e. compatible with the structure of the world. It would lead us too far here to discuss these measuring prescriptions thoroughly in the case of a length measurement. It may suffice here to raise the question of a length of 10^{-100} cm in order to show that physical length is *not a sharply defined* concept.

This example shows something else—namely, that most "physical facts" are described by terms (e.g. length) which already presuppose a "theory"; not the theory of the field of objects to be investigated (i.e. in quantum theory, the field of atoms and molecules) but the theory of other, previously investigated, fields. Thus, for investigating atomic structures, apparatus must be used the construction of which would be impossible without the knowledge of the physical processes in such an apparatus—for example, without a knowledge of Maxwellian electrodynamics.

It would go far beyond the scope of this book to treat all these problems of the definition of physical concepts. Here we propose to show two facts: first that physical concepts are not accurately definable and, secondly, that in this book we cannot attack the problem of elucidating the structure of all physical concepts used. Consequently, we may be permitted not to go into the significance of many physical terms used (it may be expected that the reader knows these terms) or to refer to them in only a few brief words.

If the mathematical field (1) uses only accurately defined terms but the physical field (2) uses terms that are always associated with uncertainties, the correlation prescriptions (3) cannot be absolutely sharp either, but must always contain at least the uncertainty inherent in (2). Thus, (3) never forms a (mathematically so-called) isomorphous correlation since this can never apply between two fields as different as (1) and (2). However, this does not mean at all that (1) cannot be used to describe (2); on the contrary, (1) always "simplifies" the situation in (2) and thereby makes it accessible to our comprehension.

This short sketch may suffice for our discussion of the development of the quantum theory given below. However, before we enter into the details of this development we wish to make a few fundamental remarks on the relationship of a systematic and deductive account to the historical, more inductive, development of a theory. The fact that we give this beforehand and not afterwards as a consequence of the development described will in fact facilitate our understanding of this historical development.

The aim of a deductive synthesis of a theory is to understand the theory in its very structure more accurately by discovering the basic structures—often also called axioms in the physical field (2)—from which the whole theory can be constructed. It may then be possible to determine more accurately which of these fundamental structures no longer correspond to reality in other fields. A simple example of a deductive synthesis is thermodynamics when this is traced back to the first and second laws as basic structures.

On the other hand, historical development starts out from the primary desire to find for the first time a theory for a field of experience not yet theoretically explained, regardless of how this aim may be achieved: here success alone justifies the method.

While in deductive synthesis a distinction is made between the axioms and the structures deduced from them, the historical development often represents a guess at the theory from part-structures deduced from experience. The serious misconception that historical development deduces the required theory from the experimental results is widespread; or frequently, as the opposite of this opinion: it is known from the historical development that the theory cannot be deduced, i.e. does not necessarily follow, from the experimental results presented and from this the conclusion is drawn that the theory may or must therefore be false ("may" or "must" according to the temperament of the "critic"). For example, the special relativity theory cannot be *deduced* from the Michelson experiment, therefore this theory is taken to be false or at least could be false. Historically, the

Michelson experiment in fact gave only the impulse for the discovery of the special relativity theory. Without the scrupulous separation of historical development and deductive construction, an *understanding* of the ferreting out of physical theories is impossible—in fact, the discovery of new theories will generally be made quite impossible, since a new theory is faced with experimental results that have not yet been explained and which almost always do not by any means represent the basic structures of a deductive synthesis that can be formulated in the *axioms*. These basic structures are, rather, from the experimental point of view, almost always so general and so comprehensive in their statements (e.g. in thermodynamics: there is no experimental possibility of constructing a perpetual motion machine of the second kind) that as such they are as good as incapable of being directly verified experimentally (at the most they are capable of being directly falsified in certain physical fields).

The historical development of the quantum theory shows us one—no, better, two—routes, neither of which followed the path of deductive synthesis but which led to the same final result. Consequently, this development can be very informative for us.

CHAPTER II

The Two Routes to Quantum Mechanics

IN THIS book those papers are reprinted (partially, in the form of extracts) which, in the first place, took the decisive last steps on the route via point mechanics to quantum mechanics and, in the second place, travelled via a wave field to a "wave mechanics" that is equivalent to quantum mechanics. It is our desire to sketch both routes briefly in retrospect so that the original papers given can be seen better in a broader relationship.

§ 1. The Particle Picture of Classical Mechanics

The discovery of electrons, the deflection experiments, and the determination of the electronic charge and mass permitted classical point mechanics to appear as a suitable means of describing all these processes; no new theory appeared to be necessary for this purpose. Since the second route to wave mechanics used the same starting-point, this classical model of electrons as mass points may be briefly sketched.

According to this model, the "orbits" of the electrons are derived from the Lagrangian variational principle:

$$W = \int_{t_1}^{t_2} L\, dt \tag{II.1}$$

must be made an extreme (stationary) value; in

$$L = \sum_{k=1}^{n} \sum_{\nu=1}^{3} \left[\frac{m}{2} \dot{x}_\nu^{(k)} \dot{x}_\nu^{(k)} + \frac{e}{c} \dot{x}_\nu^{(k)} A_\nu(x^{(k)}, t) - e\varphi(x^{(k)}, t) \right] - \frac{1}{2} \sum_{\substack{k,l \\ (k \neq l)}} \frac{e^2}{r_{(k,l)}} \tag{II.2}$$

the coordinates $x_\nu^{(k)}(t)$ ($\nu = 1, 2, 3; k = 1, 2, \cdots n$) of the n electrons in the form $x_\nu^{(k)}(t) + \varepsilon\xi_\nu^{(k)}(t)$ are to be varied with the auxiliary condition $\xi_\nu^{(k)}(t_1) = \xi_\nu^{(k)}(t_2) = 0$, i.e. we must put $\left(\frac{dW}{d\varepsilon}\right)_{\varepsilon=0} = 0$ for otherwise arbitrary $\xi_\nu^{(k)}(t)$.

In (II.2) m is the electronic mass and e is the electronic charge, $r_{(k,l)}$ is the distance between the lth and kth electrons, φ is the scalar and A_ν is the vector potential of the external electromagnetic field in which the electrons move.

In (II.2) we have neglected the magnetic field of the moving electrons, as well as all relativistic effects, which is a good approximation when the electrons are moving slowly in comparison with the velocity of light. Then, from (II.2) the Euler equations

$$m\ddot{x}_\nu^{(k)} = eE_\nu(x^{(k)}, t) + \sum_{\mu=1}^{3} \frac{e}{c} B_{\nu\mu}(x^{(k)}, t)\, \dot{x}_\mu^{(k)}, \qquad \nu = 1, 2, 3, \qquad \text{(II.3)}$$

follow with

$$E_\nu(x, t) = \varphi_{|\nu}(x, t) - \frac{1}{c}\dot{A}_\nu(x, t) - \left(\sum_k \frac{e}{r_{(k)}}\right)_{|\nu}$$

$$r_{(k)}^2 = \sum_{\nu=1}^{3}(x_\nu - x_\nu^{(k)})^2, \qquad \text{(II.4)}$$

$$B_{\nu\mu}(x, t) = A_{\mu|\nu}(x, t) - A_{\nu|\mu}(x, t).$$

E_ν are the components of the electric field and $B_{\nu\mu}$ those of the magnetic field, the components of the magnetic field vector B_ν^* being given $B_1^* = B_{23}$ (and cyclically). These equations (relativistically generalized) are the basis even today for the construction of modern accelerators, since quantum-mechanical effects are not involved in the motion of the particles in these devices.

Point mechanics appeared to represent experience correctly until, on the basis of the Rutherford model of the atom, these equations were also applied to the motion of the electrons round the atomic nucleus. Before we go into this, we may briefly sketch *classical* mechanics in its Hamilton–Jacobi form, since it is just in this form that it became the starting point of both routes to quantum theory.

We shall denote the $x_\nu^{(k)}$ numbered throughout by q_i, or regard the q_i as differentiable functions $q_i = f_i(x_1^{(1)} \cdots x_3^{(n)})$ of the $x_\nu^{(k)}$ the inverse of which are defined unambiguously. In that case, therefore,

$$L = L(q_1, q_2, \cdots, \dot{q}_1, \cdots, t) = L(q, \dot{q}, t).$$

The Euler equations of the variational problem (II.2) then have the well-known Lagrangian form

$$\frac{\partial L}{\partial q_i} - \frac{d}{dt}\frac{\partial L}{\partial \dot{q}_i} = 0. \tag{II.5}$$

If in addition to the q_i, y_i are introduced as new independent variables such that $\dot{q}_i = y_i$, instead of (II.1) we can also demand

$$\int_{t_1}^{t_2} L(q, y, t)\, dt = \text{extremum} \tag{II.6}$$

under the auxiliary condition $y_i - \dot{q}_i = 0$.

By means of Lagrangian parameters $\lambda_i(t)$, (II.6) is converted into

$$\int_{t_1}^{t_2} [L(q, y, t) - \sum_i \lambda_i(y_i - \dot{q}_i)]\, dt = \text{extremum} \tag{II.7}$$

in which the q_i, y_i, and λ_i are to be varied. By variation of the y_i, in particular, we obtain

$$\frac{\partial L}{\partial y_i} - \lambda_i = 0. \tag{II.8}$$

If (II.8) is substituted in (II.7), we obtain the problem equivalent to (II.7)

$$\int_{t_1}^{t_2} \left[L - \sum_i \frac{\partial L}{\partial y_i}(y_i - \dot{q}_i)\right] dt = \text{extremum}. \tag{II.9}$$

The transition from the y_i to the p_i variables which are canonically conjugate to the q_i by means of

$$p_i = \frac{\partial L(q, y, t)}{\partial y_i} \tag{II.10}$$

is important; here it is assumed that the determinant

$$\left| \frac{\partial^2 L}{\partial y_i \, \partial y_k} \right| \neq 0.$$

From (II.9) we obtain by means of the Hamilton function

$$H(p, q, t) = \sum_i p_i y_i - L \tag{II.11}$$

the canonical form of the variational problem:

$$\int_{t_1}^{t_2} [- H + \sum_i p_i \dot{q}_i] \, dt = \text{extremum} \tag{II.12}$$

and from this the Hamiltonian equations of motion in the form of Euler equations:

$$\dot{p}_i = - \frac{\partial H}{\partial q_i}, \qquad \dot{q}_i = \frac{\partial H}{\partial p_i}. \tag{II.13}$$

If in (II.2) the q_i are put specially equal to the $x_\nu^{(k)}$ and the p_i are denoted correspondingly by $p_\nu^{(k)}$, we obtain

$$H(p_1^{(1)} \cdots p_3^{(n)}, x_1^{(1)} \cdots x_3^{(n)}, t)$$

$$= \sum_{k=1}^{n} \left[\sum_{\nu=1}^{3} \frac{1}{2m} \left(p_\nu^{(k)} - \frac{e}{c} A_\nu(x^{(k)}, t) \right)^2 + e\varphi(x^{(k)}, t) \right]$$

$$+ \frac{1}{2} \sum_{\substack{k, l \\ (k \neq l)}} \frac{e^2}{r_{(k, l)}}. \tag{II.14}$$

The following considerations, which were originally developed as a method for solving the Hamiltonian equations (II.13), were not only decisive for the transition to "matrix mechanics" but also for that to "wave mechanics". These considerations have the canonical transformations as starting-point. The problem is posed of introducing, in place of the p_i, q_i, other variables p_i' and q_i' such that the form of the Hamiltonian equations is preserved; this means, however, that the variational problem

$$\int_{t_1}^{t_2} [-H' + \sum_i p_i' \dot{q}_i'] \, dt = \text{extremum} \qquad \text{(II.15)}$$

must be equivalent to (II.12). This is the case at least when the integrands of (II.12) and (II.10) differ only by a total differential since the integrand is not varied at the boundary for $t = t_1$ and $t = t_2$. This condition is

$$-H \, dt + \sum_i p_i \, dq_i + H' \, dt - \sum_i p_i' dq_i' = dR'. \qquad \text{(II.16)}$$

For the sake of convention, we add $d(\sum_i p_i' q_i')$ to both sides and obtain in this way as equivalent to (II.16):

$$(H' - H) \, dt + \sum_i p_i \, dq_i + \sum_i q_i' \, dp_i' = dS. \qquad \text{(II.17)}$$

Because of the form of the left-hand side, we choose for S a function of p_i', q_i, and t. Consequently, it follows from (II.17) that:

$$p_i = \frac{\partial S}{\partial q_i}, \qquad q_i' = \frac{\partial S}{\partial p_i'}, \qquad H' = H + \frac{\partial S}{\partial t}. \qquad \text{(II.18)}$$

These equations (II.18), with any function S, form a canonical transformation when the p_i', q_i' are calculated in terms of the p_i, q_i, and conversely from (II.18). Consequently, the Hamiltonian equations

$$\dot{p}_i' = -\frac{\partial H'}{\partial q_i'}, \qquad \dot{q}_i' = \frac{\partial H'}{\partial p_i'}$$

apply. These equations can be solved immediately when we can put $H' \equiv 0$, i.e. when S satisfies the equation

$$H\left(\frac{\partial S}{\partial q_1} \cdots, q_1 \cdots, t\right) + \frac{\partial S}{\partial t} = 0. \qquad \text{(II.19)}$$

If, in fact, a solution of the Hamilton–Jacobi partial differential equation (II.19) has been found in such a way that it still depends on $N = 3n$ independent parameters p_i', a canonical transformation can be carried out with this S according to (II.18) and the p_i, q_i can be obtained as functions of the constants p_i', q_i', whereby (II.13) is completely solved.

However, the converse also applies. For example, let (II.13) be solved for all possible initial values, then the general solution of (II.19) can be constructed immediately:

For this purpose we wish to consider the q_i and p_i as functions of the *initial* values $\overset{1}{q}_i$ of the q_i at time t_1 and of the *final* values $\overset{2}{q}_i$ of the q_i at time t_2:

$$q_i = q_i\left(t;\; t_1, \overset{1}{q}, t_2, \overset{2}{q}\right),$$

$$p_i = p_i\left(t;\; t_1, \overset{1}{q}, t_2, \overset{2}{q}\right). \tag{II.20}$$

Below, for brevity, instead of $f(t_1)$ we write $[f]_1$ and $f(t_2) = [f]_2$. Consequently,

$$[q_i]_1 = \overset{1}{q}_i, \qquad [q_i]_2 = \overset{2}{q}_i.$$

If W is calculated from (II.1) or (II.12) for the case where the q_i, p_i are replaced by the expressions (II.20), W becomes

$$W = W\left(t_1, \overset{1}{q}, t_2, \overset{2}{q}\right).$$

If we now form the total differential of W from (II.12), we obtain, in view of (II.13):

$$dW = -\left[-H + \sum_i p_i\dot{q}_i\right]_1 dt_1 + \left[-H + \sum_i p_i\dot{q}_i\right]_2 dt_2$$
$$- \left[\sum_i p_i\, dq_i\right]_1 + \left[\sum_i p_i\, dq_i\right]_2 .$$

According to (II.20)

$$dq_i = \frac{\partial q_i}{\partial t_1} dt_1 + \sum_k \frac{\partial q_i}{\partial \overset{1}{q}_k} d\overset{1}{q}_k + \frac{\partial q_i}{\partial t_2} dt_2 + \sum_R \frac{\partial q_i}{\partial \overset{2}{q}_k} d\overset{2}{q}_k;$$

since, however,

$$\overset{1}{q}_i = [q_i]_1 = q_i\left(t_1; t_1, \overset{1}{q}; t_2, \overset{2}{q}\right)$$

it follows that

$$d\overset{1}{q}_i = \left[\frac{\partial q_i}{\partial t}\right]_1 dt_1 + \left[\frac{\partial q_i}{\partial t_1}\right]_1 dt_1 + \left[\sum_k \frac{\partial q_i}{\partial \overset{1}{q}_k}\right]_1 d\overset{1}{q}_k$$

$$+ \left[\frac{\partial q_i}{\partial t_2}\right]_1 dt_2 + \left[\sum_k \frac{\partial q_i}{\partial \overset{2}{q}_k}\right]_1 d\overset{2}{q}_k$$

and therefore

$$[dq_i]_1 = d\overset{1}{q}_i - [\dot{q}_i]_1\, dt_1\,.$$

If the corresponding formula for $[dq_i]_2$ is used, we therefore obtain

$$dW = H_1\, dt_1 - H_2\, dt_2 - \sum_i [p_i]_1\, d\overset{1}{q}_i + \sum_i [p_i]_2\, d\overset{2}{q}_i\,. \qquad \text{(II.21)}$$

If we start from any surface $\mathscr{F}(q) = 0$ in the q-space and construct at each point $\overset{1}{q}_i$ of this surface a trajectory with the initial values $[q_i]_1 = \overset{1}{q}_i$ and

$$[p_i]_1 = \lambda\left(\overset{1}{q}_k\right) \frac{\partial \mathscr{F}\left(\overset{1}{q}\right)}{\partial \overset{1}{q}_i}$$

then, because of

$$\overset{1}{q}_i = q_i\left(t_1; t_1, \overset{1}{q}, t_2, \overset{2}{q}\right),$$

$\overset{1}{q}_i = \overset{1}{q}_i\left(\overset{2}{q}, t_2\right)$ becomes a function of the $\overset{2}{q}_k$, t_2, since we choose t_1 the same for all points of the surface.

For the function

$$S\left(t_2; \overset{2}{q}\right) = W\left(t_1; \overset{1}{q}_k\left(\overset{2}{q}_s, t_2\right); t_2, \overset{2}{q}\right)$$

it then follows that t_1 is constant and as $\sum \dfrac{\partial \mathscr{F}}{\partial \overset{1}{q}_i} d\overset{1}{q}_i = 0$

$$dS = -[H]_2\, dt_2 + \sum_i [p_i]_2\, d\overset{2}{q}_i\,. \qquad \text{(II.22)}$$

If we drop the index 2, $S(t; q)$ satisfies the equations:

$$\frac{\partial S}{\partial t} = - H(p, q); \qquad \frac{\partial S}{\partial q_i} = p_i .$$

Thus, a solution S of (II.19) depending on the arbitrary "initial surface" $\mathscr{F}(q_i) = 0$ has been obtained. This last relation between particle orbits and the Hamilton–Jacobi function S was important for the route to "wave mechanics".

To complete the particle picture, we may sketch the description of the one-dimensional anharmonic oscillator, which served as the first test example for the development of matrix mechanics. With $V(q)$ as potential energy,

$$H(p, q) = \frac{1}{2m} p^2 + V(q). \tag{II.23}$$

We solve (II.19) using the formula $S(q, t) = - Et + R(q)$, so that, therefore, for R it follows that

$$\frac{1}{2m}\left(\frac{dR}{dq}\right)^2 + V(q) = E. \tag{II.24}$$

If we denote E by p', we have

$$R(p', q) = \int \sqrt{2m}\,\sqrt{p' - V(q)}\, dq. \tag{II.25}$$

We shall assume that $V(q)$ tends to $+\infty$ as $q \to +\infty$ and as $q \to -\infty$. Then (II.25) is only meaningful when R is real, i.e. as long as $p' \geqq V(q)$. However, this in fact represents the energy law which gives the solutions of $E = p' = V(q_1) = V(q_2)$ as turning points q_1, q_2 of the periodic motion. The canonical transformation to be carried out with R in accordance with

$$p = \frac{\partial R}{\partial q}, \qquad q' = \frac{\partial R}{\partial p'} \tag{II.25a}$$

gives, because $H' = p'$, the equatons $\dot{p}' = 0$ and $\dot{q}' = 1$. The still undetermined sign of the square root can be defined by means of (II.25a)

$$p = \frac{\partial W}{\partial q} = \sqrt{2m}\sqrt{p' - V(q)}$$

in such a way that $p = m\dot{q}$. However, instead of $p' = E$, we introduce also the important action variable $\mathscr{J}$ according to

$$\begin{aligned} \mathscr{J}(p') &= \frac{1}{2\pi}\oint \sqrt{2m}\sqrt{p' - V(q)}\,dq \\ &= \frac{1}{2\pi}\oint \frac{\partial W}{\partial q}\,dq = \frac{1}{2\pi}\oint p\,dq = \frac{1}{2\pi}\oint dW, \end{aligned} \tag{II.26}$$

the integration having to be carried out over a complete period, i.e.

$$\begin{aligned} \mathscr{J}(p') &= \frac{1}{2\pi}\int_{q_1}^{q_2} \sqrt{2m}\sqrt{p' - V(q)}\,dq + \frac{1}{2\pi}\int_{q_2}^{q_1} \sqrt{2m}\,(-1)\sqrt{p' - V(q)}\,dq \\ &= \frac{2}{2\pi}\int_{q_1}^{q_2} \sqrt{2m}\sqrt{p' - V(q)}\,dq. \end{aligned} \tag{II.27}$$

If $R^*(\mathscr{J}, q) = R(p', q)$ it is possible to carry out the canonical transformation to the variables $\mathscr{J}, w$:

$$p = \frac{\partial R^*}{\partial q}, \qquad w = \frac{\partial R^*}{\partial \mathscr{J}}, \qquad H^*(\mathscr{J}) = p'(\mathscr{J}) = E(\mathscr{J}). \tag{II.28}$$

Thus, we have introduced the "angle variable" which is canonically conjugate to the "action variable". The canonical equations now run:

$$\dot{\mathscr{J}} = 0, \qquad \dot{w} = \frac{dE}{d\mathscr{J}}$$

with the solutions $\mathscr{J}$ = const and

$$w = \frac{dE}{d\mathscr{J}}(t - \tau). \tag{II.29}$$

From (II.27), by differentiation with respect to $\mathscr{J}$, we obtain:

$$2\pi = \frac{d}{d\mathscr{J}} 2 \int_{q_1}^{q_2} \sqrt{2m} \sqrt{p' - V(q)}\, dq$$

$$= 2\sqrt{2m} \left[\sqrt{p' - V(q_2)} \frac{dq_2}{d\mathscr{J}} - \sqrt{p' - V(q_1)} \frac{dq_1}{d\mathscr{J}} \right]$$

$$+ 2 \int_{q_1}^{q_2} \frac{\partial R^*}{\partial q\, \partial \mathscr{J}}\, dq.$$

Since $p' = V(q_1) = V(q_2)$, we have

$$2\pi = \oint \frac{\partial R^*}{\partial q\, \partial \mathscr{J}}\, dq = \oint \frac{\partial w}{\partial q}\, dq = \oint dw = \oint \dot{w}\, dt = \frac{dE}{d\mathscr{J}} T$$

with T as the period of the oscillation. $2\pi/T$ is the angular frequency ω of the motion, i.e.

$$\omega = \frac{dE}{d\mathscr{J}}. \tag{II.30}$$

In particular, for the harmonic oscillator with $V(q) = \frac{a}{2} q^2$ we have

$$E(\mathscr{J}) = \sqrt{\frac{a}{m}} \mathscr{J} = \omega \mathscr{J},$$

$$w = \arcsin \sqrt{\frac{a}{2\omega \mathscr{J}}}\, q,$$

$$p = \sqrt{2m\omega \mathscr{J} - m^2 \omega^2 q^2}. \tag{II.31}$$

§ 2. From Point Mechanics to Matrix Mechanics

The transition from point mechanics to matrix mechanics took place via Rutherford's atomic model and Bohr's atomic theory. Since a special volume of the Selected Readings in Physics by D. ter Haar is devoted to the development of Bohr's atomic theory, we need not go into it in more detail here. We shall merely sketch the essence of Bohr's atomic model briefly:

Z electrons revolve about the Z-fold positively charged atomic nucleus. The motion of the electrons is to be calculated according to the laws of point mechanics given above. For the case of multiply periodic movements it is possible to introduce a "quantum condition". Multiply periodic movements exist when it is possible to introduce such canonical variables p_i, q_i that the Hamilton–Jacobi differential equation (II.19) can be solved by the formula $S = -Et + \sum_i S_i(q_i)$, in which each S_i depends on only *one* coordinate q_i and each q_i performs a periodic motion similar to that of the anharmonic oscillator sketched above. Consequently, this anharmonic oscillator has become the model of the quantum theory. The quantum conditions then run

$$\mathcal{J}_i = \frac{1}{2\pi} \oint p_i \, dq_i = n_i \hbar, \tag{II.32}$$

in which $h = 2\pi\hbar$ is Planck's constant, the n_i are integers, and the $\mathcal{J}_i$ are the action variables. The energy, i.e. the Hamilton function after transformation to the action and angle variables $\mathcal{J}_i$, w_i then becomes a function $E(\mathcal{J}_1, \mathcal{J}_2, \cdots)$. The quantum conditions (II.32) gives a series of discrete energy values $E(n_1\hbar, n_2\hbar \cdots)$. The frequencies ω of the spectral lines emitted must then be calculated from Bohr's frequency conditions

$$\hbar\omega_{n_1 n_2 \cdots, n_1' n_2' \cdots} = E(n_1\hbar, n_2\hbar, \cdots) - E(n_1'\hbar, n_2'\hbar, \cdots). \tag{II.33}$$

For the anharmonic oscillator, we then obtain, in particular:

$$\mathcal{J} = \frac{1}{2\pi} \oint \sqrt{2m} \sqrt{E - V(q)} \, dq = n\hbar \tag{II.34}$$

and from this the discrete values of the energy

$$E_n = E(\mathcal{J})_{\mathcal{J} = n\hbar} = E(n\hbar). \tag{II.35}$$

The emitted frequencies would then be

$$\hbar\omega_{n,m} = E_n - E_m. \tag{II.36}$$

The next problem that arose was calculating the intensities of the lines emitted according to (II.33) or (II.36). Since the following considerations do not depend on the number of degrees of freedom, we can stay with the case of the anharmonic oscillator. Since the motion of q and p and of all unique functions of q and p takes place periodically with frequency ω, we can expand this in a Fourier series:

$$q = \sum_{\nu=-\infty}^{+\infty} q_\nu(\mathcal{J})\, e^{i\nu\omega(t-\tau)} = \sum_{\nu=-\infty}^{+\infty} q_\nu(\mathcal{J})\, e^{i\nu w},$$

$$p = \sum_{\nu=-\infty}^{+\infty} p_\nu(\mathcal{J})\, e^{i\nu w},$$

$$F(p, q) = \sum_{\nu=-\infty}^{+\infty} F_\nu(\mathcal{J})\, e^{i\nu w}. \tag{II.37}$$

For real F, therefore, $F_{-\nu} = F_\nu^*$.

The energy emitted per unit time is, as is well known, obtained classically in accordance with Hertzian dipole radiation as

$$\mathscr{E} = \frac{2e^2}{3c^3}\,\overline{|\ddot{q}|^2} = \frac{4e^2}{3c^3}\sum_{\nu=1}^{\infty} |q_\nu(\mathcal{J})|^2\,(\nu\omega)^4, \tag{II.38}$$

i.e. it is composed additively of the contributions for the individual frequencies $\nu\omega$:

$$\mathscr{E}_\nu = \frac{4e^2}{3c^3}\,|q_\nu(\mathcal{J})|^2\,(\nu\omega)^4. \tag{II.39}$$

These classical results were transformed by Bohr into quantum-theoretical results by means of the principle which he called the correspondence principle by carrying out the following substitutions in (II.39),

$$\nu\omega \longrightarrow \omega_{nm}, \quad \nu \longrightarrow n - m, \quad \mathcal{J} \rightarrow n'\hbar, \tag{II.40}$$

with n' between n and m. Because the value of n' cannot be defined accurately, (II.40) cannot represent the exact quantum theory. But it is just these considerations, which were also extended by Kramers and Born to other problems, that were the starting-point of Heisenberg's formula of matrix mechanics.

The decisive idea expressed in the very introduction of Heisenberg's paper is the abandonment of any classical—"point-mechanical"—description and therefore the transition to the corresponding quantum-mechanical magnitudes, the abandonment of the orbits which are "unobservable" in principle and therefore the transition to the quantum-mechanical transition amplitudes describing the observations. Heisenberg's arguments also lead directly to the conditions (II.32) and (II.34) of Bohr's theory. We shall briefly recapitulate this argument on the basis of his paper:

The decisive starting-point is Bohr's frequency condition

$$\nu(n, n - \alpha) = \frac{1}{h}\{W(n) - W(n - \alpha)\},$$

in our notation (II.36). This frequency condition had proved very valuable since it permitted Einstein's hypothesis of light quanta, which was based on Planck's relation for the energy quanta $\hbar\omega$ of a harmonic oscillator, to be connected through the energy law with the discrete energy values of an atomic system shown to exist by the Frank–Hertz collision experiments.

Heisenberg compared (II.30) with the certainly correct quantum-mechanical formula (II.36), by assigning to the classical harmonics $(n - m)\omega$ a frequency ω_{nm}:

classical: $$(n - m)\omega = (n - m)\frac{dE}{d\mathcal{J}},$$

quantum-mechanical: $$\omega_{nm} = \frac{1}{\hbar}(E_n - E_m).$$

The comparison $\omega_{nm} \longleftrightarrow (n - m)\,\omega$ appears logical just in this way, since then the quantum-theoretical and classical combination relations corresponded to one another (p. 171).

For $n - m = 1$, we should then obtain:

$$\omega(\mathscr{J}) \longleftrightarrow \omega_{r,r-1} = \frac{1}{\hbar}(E_r - E_{r-1}) = \frac{1}{\hbar}(E(\mathscr{J}_r) - E(\mathscr{J}_{r-1}))$$

$$= \frac{1}{\hbar}\left(\frac{dE}{d\mathscr{J}}\right)_{\mathscr{J}=\mathscr{J}'}(\mathscr{J}_r - \mathscr{J}_{r-1}) = \omega(\mathscr{J}')\frac{\mathscr{J}_r - \mathscr{J}_{r-1}}{\hbar}$$

with an intermediate value $\mathscr{J}'$ of $\mathscr{J}_r$ and $\mathscr{J}_{r-1}$ and $\mathscr{J}$ approximately equal to $\mathscr{J}'$. This makes it obvious to postulate

$$\mathscr{J}_r - \mathscr{J}_{r-1} = \hbar$$

which leads generally to

$$\mathscr{J}_r = r\hbar + \mathscr{J}_0. \tag{II.41}$$

(II.41) is, however, just (II.34) apart from the undetermined constant $\mathscr{J}_0$. The uncertainty with respect to $\mathscr{J}_0$ was, however, an indeterminacy of Bohr's theory that had been noted previously. Nevertheless, it was just the decisive point for Heisenberg's ideas to use no longer the magnitude $\mathscr{J}$ defined classically by (II.34) but to treat seriously the transition to purely quantum-theoretical magnitudes. This was done by using equation (II.39) in its purely quantum-theoretical form

$$\mathscr{E}_{nm} = \frac{4e^2}{3c^3}|q_{nm}|^2\,\omega_{nm}^4 \tag{II.42}$$

and consistently replacing the classical Fourier amplitudes $q_\nu(\mathscr{J})$ by the quantum-theoretical amplitudes q_{nm}, which was done not only at the expense of the fact that a Fourier series could no longer be constructed with the q_{nm} but also the fact that it is just this that is regarded as a characteristic of the unobservability of a $q(t)$.

All the rest follows almost necessarily:
The classical $q_\nu(\mathscr{J})\, e^{i\nu\omega(t-\tau)}$ are replaced by

$$Q_{nm}(t) = q_{nm}e^{i\omega_{nm}(t-\tau)};$$

the reality condition $q_\nu = q_{-\nu}^*$ by

$$q_{nm} = q_{mn}^* \quad \text{and} \quad Q_{nm} = Q_{mn}^*;$$

the relation $p = imv\omega q_v$, following from $p = m\dot{q}$, by

$$p_{rs} = im\omega_{rs}q_{rs}$$

or, if

$$\mathscr{P}_{rs} = p_{rs}e^{i\omega_{rs}(t-\tau)},$$

$$\mathscr{P}_{rs} = im\omega_{rs}Q_{rs} = m\dot{Q}_{rs}.$$

From the product of two Fourier series

$$q(t)^2 = \sum_{v,\mu} q_v q_\mu e^{i(v+\mu)\omega(t-\tau)} = \sum_{\lambda}\left(\sum_{\substack{v,\mu\\(v+\mu=\lambda)}} q_v q_\mu\right) e^{i\lambda\omega(t-\tau)}$$

and changing $l\omega = (v + \mu)\omega = v\omega + \mu\omega$ to $\omega_{rs} + \omega_{sv} = \omega_{rv}$ it is found that we must put

$$(q^2)_{rv} = \sum_s q_{rs}q_{sv} \tag{II.43}$$

This is used for $\dot{q}^2$ and therefore equation (16) given in Heisenberg's paper

$$m\sum_s\{|q_{rs}|^2\,\omega_{sr} - \omega_{rs}\,|q_{rs}|^2\} = \hbar$$

follows from (II.41), and in the subsequent paper by Born and Jordan this then acquires the final form

$$\sum_s (p_{rs}q_{st} - q_{rs}p_{st}) = \frac{\hbar}{i}\,\delta_{rt} \tag{II.44}$$

and forms one of the foundations of quantum mechanics as Heisenberg commutation relation.

Heisenberg then tested the new method on the theory of the anharmonic oscillator. The quantum-theoretical magnitudes q_{rs}, p_{rs}, and so on, can be practically guessed for the harmonic oscillator from the classical description: from (II.31) and (II.41) we can guess

$$E_n = E_0 + n\hbar\omega.$$

From the "Fourier series": $q = q_1e^{i\omega t} + q_1^*\,e^{--i\omega t}$ and $E = 2m\omega^2 q_1^2$ it is guessed that all $q_{rs} = 0$ except for

$$q_{r,r-1} = \sqrt{\frac{(r+\sigma)\,\hbar}{2m\omega}}$$

and since $q_{rs} = q_{sr}^*$:

$$q_{r,r+1} = \sqrt{\frac{(r+1+\sigma)\hbar}{2m\omega}}$$

with a still unknown σ. If the lowest energy value is denoted by the index 0, it follows from $p_{rs} = i\omega_{rs} m q_{rs}$, i.e. from

$$p_{r,r-1} = i\omega m q_{r,r-1} = i\sqrt{\frac{(r+\sigma)\hbar m\omega}{2}},$$

that (II.43) is only satisfied when we put $\sigma = 0$. The quantum-theoretical elements H_{rs} of the energy $H = \frac{1}{2m}p^2 + \frac{\omega^2 m}{2}q^2$ then become

$$H_{rs} = \delta_{rs}\hbar\omega(r + \tfrac{1}{2}),$$

i.e. the energy values must be written as

$$E_n = \hbar\omega(n + \tfrac{1}{2}).$$

The solutions for the quantum-theoretical quantities in the case of the harmonic oscillator have been deduced.

What are the quantum-theoretical quantities that replace the classical quantities such as p, q, and so on? This question is answered by Born and Jordan in the next paper from which extracts are printed: the p_{rs}, q_{rs}, and F_{rs} form the elements of matrices, and the rules of calculation are those of matrices.

Since the rules of calculation of matrices may be assumed to be known, the decisive results of the Born–Jordan paper can be summarized rapidly:

The matrices p, q must satisfy the commutation relation (II.43):

$$pq - qp = \frac{\hbar}{i}1. \tag{II.45}$$

The temporal change of any one matrix g formed from p, q is given by the fundamental dynamic equation

$$\dot{g} = \frac{i}{\hbar}(Hg - gH) \tag{II.46}$$

where H is the Hamiltonian matrix which for the anharmonic oscillator is the following functions of p, q

$$H = \frac{1}{2m} p^2 + V(q). \tag{II.47}$$

A solution of the fundamental dynamic equation (II.46) is obtained when H is represented as a diagonal matrix, since then (II.46) assumes the form

$$\dot{g}_{rs} = \frac{i}{\hbar}(E_r g_{rs} - E_s g_{rs})$$

with the solution

$$g_{rs}(t) = g_{rs}(0)\, e^{(i/\hbar)(E_r - E_s)t}.$$

It is shown for the harmonic oscillator that the matrices for p and q are determined essentially by the commutation relation and the diagonal form of H. Thus, it is shown that (II.45) and (II.46) form the foundation of matrix mechanics and satisfactorily define it.

In this way was the mathematical system deduced that can be used as the pattern of atomic structures and has proved useful as such in an absolutely unforeseeable manner. Naturally, this mathematical system still required development and a convenient mathematical form. However, this is a problem of mathematical technique. Hilbert space has proved to provide a suitable framework with the operators in the Hilbert space in place of the matrices. It cannot be the object of this small book to give an introduction into the mathematics of Hilbert space and operators. Since there are adequate textbooks on the subject today, a knowledge of the most important of these mathematical structures will be assumed.

As we shall see in more detail in Chapter III, in the terminology of Hilbert space we can regard (II.45) and (II.46) as operator equations and the question of energy values (as the diagonal elements of H as diagonal matrix) as a question of the eigenvalues of the energy operator. However, before we follow this idea further, we shall consider the second route from point mechanics to wave mechanics. This second route is also important because of the question of physical interpretation, i.e. because of the question of the directions for correlation given under (3) (p. 4). For however well the mathematical system can be characterized by (II.45) and (II.46), the physical interpretation is not known in a systematic manner but only fragmentarily, although Heisenberg himself started from the fundamental ideas of using only "observable" magnitudes. In fact, it is known that the diagonal elements of H (or, in the terminology of Hilbert space, the eigenvalues of H) represent the possible energy values of the atomic system, and that the intensities of the spectral lines can be calculated by means of the matrix elements of q and p (with H a diagonal matrix). However, all these are special cases of the interpretation; there is as yet no systematically clear prescription for the correlation between the mathematical system and physical measurements of atomic systems.

§ 3. From Point Mechanics to Wave Mechanics

A quite different route started from the initiative of de Broglie. The impulse for this was the fact that Planck's formula $E = h\nu = \hbar\omega$ (e.g. for light quanta) in combination with the special theory of relativity made an extension necessary. The form of this process of thought in de Broglie's paper is still based on the method of representing the relativity theory used at that time. The difficulty to decide between the frequency ν_1 and ν described in Chapter 1, § 1, of his paper is also explained in this way. In fact, a distinction must be made between two ideas:

1. the frequency ν_0 (according to $h\nu_0 = m_0c^2$) is the frequency of the particle's "own clock", or
2. the frequency ν_0 is the frequency of an oscillation process in space and time, i.e. of a wave, to be ascribed to the particle.

Idea 1 is used for the frequencies of an "internal" motion of the particle: if, for example, ν_0 is an eigenfrequency of an atom at rest (i.e. $h\nu_0$ is equal to the energy difference between two atomic states), $\nu_1 = \nu_0\sqrt{1-\beta^2}$ is the frequency of an atom moving with respect to the observer.

Idea 2 is, however, the correct one for the "external" motion of the particle (i.e. also for the motion of the centre of mass of the atom). This latter idea, of assigning a wave to the moving particle, then led de Broglie to his final result. In Chapter 2, § 5, he gives the decisive relation between the wave-four-vector O_i and the energy momentum vector J_i in the form $J_i = hO_i$. For the special case of the free particle, therefore, the wave $e^{i\sum_i k_j x^j}$ with $J_i = \hbar k_i$ would have to be assigned to the particle with the energy momentum vector J_i. De Broglie shows how this idea is capable of explaining some of the known quantum phenomena. The detection of the interference of electrons, by which the de Broglie relation for the spatial part of the vector

$$mv = \hbar k, \quad \text{i.e.} \quad mv = \frac{\hbar}{\lambda} \tag{II.48}$$

(with λ as wavelength) was confirmed, made it necessary to regard the supplementation of Planck's formula, $E = h\nu$, by (II.48) as confirmed. Of course, there could still be no mention of a complete theory of this wave phenomenon in de Broglie's paper; the arguments of this paper, in particular, show that they could only make the Bohr–Sommerfeld relations (II.32) plausible. Nevertheless, a very important step had been taken, since notwithstanding the different nature of particle and wave de Broglie dared to describe them as possible alternatives.

Schrödinger succeeded in completing this wave picture mathematically. The route to his famous wave equation

$$\nabla^2\psi + \frac{2m}{K^2}\left(E + \frac{e^2}{r}\right)\psi = 0$$

(for an electron in the field of the nucleus of the hydrogen atom) was still somewhat obscure in his first paper, so that he devoted the bulk of his second paper to this point. Consequently, we shall begin directly with these later considerations.

They are connected with the Hamilton–Jacobi equation (II.19). We particularize this for the case in which H does not depend explicitly on the time by means of the formula already used for the anharmonic oscillator on p. 15:

$$S = -Et + R(q) \tag{II.49}$$

and obtain for R the time-independent equation

$$H\left(\frac{\partial R}{\partial q_1}\cdots, q_1\cdots\right) = E. \tag{II.50}$$

The function $R(q)$ can be represented in q-space by the family of surfaces $R(q) = \text{const.}$ Equation (II.49) can then be interpreted in such a way that the surfaces $S = \text{const.}$ move in time t over the various surfaces $R = \text{const.}$ This has great similarity with the movement of surfaces of the same phase in a wave motion.

If in the considerations leading to (II.22) we select the parameter $\lambda\left(\overset{1}{q}\right)$ in such a way that $H\left(\overset{1}{p}, \overset{1}{q}\right) = E$, i.e. so that the energy H is constant over the whole surface $\mathscr{F}(q) = 0$, we shall have

$$S\left(t_2; \overset{2}{q}\right) = W\left(t_1; \overset{1}{q}\left(\overset{2}{q}, t_2\right), t_2, \overset{2}{q}\right)$$

according to (II.22) since $[H]_2 = H\left(\overset{2}{p}, \overset{2}{q}\right) = H\left(\overset{1}{p}, \overset{1}{q}\right) = E$ of the form (II.49), i.e. starting from a "phase surface" $\mathscr{F}(q) = 0$ at time t_1, the phase surface at time t_2 can easily be obtained after solving the equations of motion from $\int_{t_1}^{t_2} L\,dt$. Since $p_i = \partial S/\partial q_i$, the p_i are exactly "perpendicular" to the phase surfaces. If, therefore, we move from the surface from each point $\overset{1}{q}_k$ on the path $q_k(t)$ over a fixed distance $\int_{t_1}^{t_2} L\,dt = C$ we just come to the new phase surface. If $\int_{t_1}^{t_2} L\,dt$ is interpreted as the "distance" between $\overset{1}{q}$ and $\overset{2}{q}$, the "phase surfaces" can be interpreted as surfaces of equal distance.

However, this analogy of the surfaces $S = \text{const.}$ to the phase surfaces of an actual wave motion goes much deeper mathematically than we have just sketched:

Let us consider an "almost plane" wave of the form

$$\psi = e^{\frac{i}{\alpha} S(q,t)} \tag{II.51}$$

with $S(q, t) = -\alpha\omega t + R(q)$, where α is a constant that can still be freely chosen and $R(q)$ (in which the q_i are equal to the $x_j^{(k)}$) depends "almost linearly" on the q_i; in the case of a plane wave $R(q)$ would depend exactly linearly on the q_i. "Almost linear" is intended to mean that in what follows we can neglect second and higher derivatives of $R(q)$ with respect to q_i.

The "wave vector"

$$k_j = \frac{\partial R}{\partial q_j} \tag{II.52}$$

also depends only weakly on the q_i.

A linear wave equation can always be written in the form

$$W\left(\frac{\alpha}{i}\frac{\partial}{\partial q}, q, -\frac{\alpha}{i}\frac{\partial}{\partial t}\right)\psi = 0. \tag{II.53}$$

If (II.51) is substituted under the assumption made, we obtain

$$W\left(\alpha\frac{\partial R}{\partial q_1}, \cdots, q_1, \cdots, \alpha\omega\right) = 0 \tag{II.54}$$

and with (II.52):

$$W(\alpha k, q, \alpha\omega) = 0. \tag{II.55}$$

If (II.54) and (II.55) are solved for $\alpha\omega$, we obtain

$$\alpha\omega = \bar{H}\left(\alpha\frac{\partial R}{\partial q_1}\cdots, q_1\cdots\right) \tag{II.56}$$

and

$$\alpha\omega = \bar{H}(\alpha k, q), \tag{II.57}$$

respectively. For $H = \bar{H}$, (II.56) is identical with equation (II.50) if, following Planck and de Broglie, (II.48) is written with

$\alpha = \hbar : \hbar\omega = E$, and $\hbar k_i = p_i = \dfrac{\partial R}{\partial q_i}$. The formula for the group velocity v_i of a wave packet (also used by de Broglie and Schrödinger in their papers)

$$v_i = \frac{\partial \omega}{\partial k_i}$$

then becomes

$$v_i = \frac{1}{\alpha}\frac{\partial \bar{H}}{\partial k_i} = \frac{\partial \bar{H}}{\partial(\alpha k_i)} = \frac{\partial H}{\partial p_i} = \dot{q}_i. \tag{II.58}$$

Likewise, it then follows that:

$$\alpha \dot{k}_i = \alpha \frac{d}{dt}\frac{\partial R}{\partial q_i} = \alpha \sum_j \frac{\partial^2 R}{\partial q_i\, \partial q_j}\dot{q}_j = \alpha \sum_j \frac{\partial^2 R}{\partial q_i\, \partial q_j}\frac{\partial \bar{H}}{\partial(\alpha k_j)}.$$

From (II.56) we obtain by differentiation with respect to q_i:

$$0 = \frac{\partial \bar{H}}{\partial q_i} + \sum_j \frac{\partial \bar{H}}{\partial(\alpha k_j)}\alpha \frac{\partial^2 R}{\partial q_j\, \partial q_i},$$

so that, therefore,

$$\alpha \dot{k}_i = -\frac{\partial \bar{H}}{\partial q_i}$$

which, since $\alpha k_i = \hbar k_i = p_i$, becomes identical with the second Hamiltonian equation.

The route back from (II.56) to the wave equation (II.53) is, of course, not unambiguous. If, in fact, the relation

$$\psi = e^{-i\omega t}\varphi(q), \tag{II.59}$$

is assumed, in which $\varphi(q)$ no longer needs to be an "almost-plane" wave, $\varphi(q)$ must, according to (II.53), satisfy the time-independent wave equation (with $\alpha = \hbar$ and $\hbar\omega = E$)

$$W\left(\frac{\hbar}{i}\frac{\partial}{\partial q_1}\cdots, q_1 \cdots, E\right)\varphi(q) = 0. \tag{II.60}$$

The simplest possiblity for (II.60) is

$$H\left(\frac{\hbar}{i}\frac{\partial}{\partial q_1}\cdots, q_1 \cdots\right)\varphi(q) = E\varphi(q), \tag{II.61}$$

where, in the classical expression for H, the momentum p_i has been replaced in a "suitable" manner by $\frac{\hbar}{i}\frac{\partial}{\partial q_i}$. The suitable manner has been found with the aid of (II.14) to have the form (with $q_i = x_i$):

$$H\left(\frac{\hbar}{i}\frac{\partial}{\partial q_1}\cdots, q_1\cdots\right) = \sum_{j=1}^{3}\frac{1}{2m}\left(\frac{\hbar}{i}\frac{\partial}{\partial x_j} - \frac{e}{c}A_\nu(x)\right)^2 + e\varphi(x) \qquad \text{(II.62)}$$

in which, in the first instance, the fields A_ν and φ must be assumed to be constant with time.

In his fourth communication, Schrödinger then also attempted the step to the time-dependent wave equation which, in a manner exactly parallel with the above considerations with the assumption (II.51), can be made plausible only if we do not only put $S(q, t) = -\alpha\omega t + R(q)$ but with time-dependent external fields we make $\partial S/\partial t$ weakly dependent on the q_i and t. Then, in the same way as above, we obtain as the "simplest" possibility, instead of (II.61)

$$H\left(\frac{\hbar}{i}\frac{\partial}{\partial q_1}\cdots, q_1\cdots, t\right)\psi = -\frac{\hbar}{i}\frac{\partial\psi}{\partial t} \qquad \text{(II.63)}$$

with the same H according to (II.62), the A_ν and φ also possibly being time-dependent.

At this point, the agreement of the solutions for the energy values by matrix mechanics on the one hand and by wave mechanics on the other hand was astonishing. Schrödinger was able to solve the most important problems (harmonic oscillator, hydrogen atom) directly. Schrödinger's paper is—even when considered in retrospect from the standpoint of today—so clear that it is superfluous to add even one more word to it.

Matrix mechanics and wave mechanics appear in some way to be at least partially equivalent; the physical significance of wave mechanics and matrix mechanics is given only in partial aspects and frequently very uncertainly, so that both the problem of equivalence and that of the physical explanation require a thorough systematic investigation. Schrödinger gave the solution to the first of the two problems. Consequently, we shall also turn first to this problem and summarize Schrödinger's results in the modern terminology of Hilbert space.

CHAPTER III

Matrix Mechanics and Wave Mechanics as Representations of Mathematical Structures in Hilbert Space

THE famous paper by Schrödinger, "Über das Verhältnis der Heisenberg–Born–Jordanschen Quantenmechanik zu der meinen" ["On the relationship of the Heisenberg–Born–Jordan quantum mechanics to mine"], shows the mathematical isomorphism of the two theories. It is customary today to consider the two forms of the theory as concrete representations of an abstract Hilbert space structure. If we denote matrix mechanics by $\mathscr{M}$, wave mechanics by $\mathscr{W}$, and the abstract Hilbert space structure by $\mathscr{H}$, Schrödinger therefore shows that $\mathscr{M} \longleftrightarrow \mathscr{W}$, in which $\longleftrightarrow$ may denote an isomorphous mapping. Today it is customary to regard $\mathscr{H} \longleftrightarrow \mathscr{W}$ and $\mathscr{H} \longleftrightarrow \mathscr{M}$ and many other representations $\mathscr{H} \longleftrightarrow \mathscr{R}$ in such a way that $\mathscr{W}$ and $\mathscr{M}$ are only special cases of many possible $\mathscr{R}$. In this method of considering the situation, the isomorphism $\mathscr{W} \longleftrightarrow \mathscr{M}$ is of course retained.

When we speak of isomorphism, we must say with respect to what structures isomorphism exists. Such an isomorphism is most frequent in analytical geometry, in which an isomorphous assignment of certain analytical expressions to geometrical structures is investigated. The situation is similar here. The Hilbert space is an abstract complex vector space with an internal product. The rules of calculation for this vector space we assume to be known.

Consequently, we shall summarize them only briefly here. The elements of a Hilbert space $u, v, \cdots$ can be added like vectors and be multiplied by complex numbers α, β, $\cdots$, whereupon the following equations, for example, hold:

$$\alpha(u + v) = \alpha u + \alpha v,$$

$$(\alpha + \beta)\, u = \alpha u + \beta u.$$

In addition, an internal product (u, v) = complex number, is defined by

$$(u_1 + u_2, v) = (u_1, v) + (u_2, v)$$

$$(u, v) = (v, u)^*, \quad (u, \alpha v) = \alpha(u, v), \quad (u, u) \geqq 0,$$

and $(u, u) = 0$ has the consequence $u = 0$.

Two vectors z and v with $(u, v) = 0$ are called orthogonal. We call a set u_i of vectors with $(u_i, u_k) = \delta_{ik}$ ($\delta_{ik} = 0$ for $i \neq k$ and $\delta_{ii} = 1$) and with $\sum_{i=1}^{n} \alpha_i u_i$ everywhere dense in the Hilbert space a complete orthonormal system (below denoted by c.o.s. for short); i.e. for any vector v and given $\varepsilon > 0$ there are numbers α_i and n with

$$\left\| v - \sum_{i=1}^{n} \alpha_i u_i \right\| < \varepsilon,$$

the norm $\|u\|$ being defined by $\|u\|^2 = (u, u)$. The degree of such a complete orthonormal system can be called the dimension of a Hilbert space, since all c.o.s. of a Hilbert space have the same degree.

With fixed n, $\left\| v - \sum_{i=1}^{n} \alpha_i u_i \right\|$ is smallest,† if we take

$$\alpha_i = (u_i, v);$$

† Because of the orthogonality of the two summands of the right-hand side it follows from

$$v - \sum_{i=1}^{n} \lambda_i u_i = \left[v - \sum_{i=1}^{n} u_i(u_i, v) \right] + \left[\sum_{i=1}^{n} u_i((u_i, v) - \lambda_i) \right]$$

that

$$\left\| v - \sum_{i=1}^{n} \lambda_i u_i \right\|^2 = \left\| v - \sum_{i=1}^{n} u_i(u_i, v) \right\|^2 + \sum_{i=1}^{n} |(u_i, v) - \lambda_i|^2.$$

consequently we have $\left\| v + \sum_{i=1}^{n} u_i(u_i, v) \right\| \underset{n}{\to} 0$ which can also be written as

$$v = \sum_{i=1}^{\infty} u_i(u_i, v).$$

The dimension of the Hilbert space below we assume to be always countably infinite. If we consider only the structures just given, all Hilbert spaces of the same dimension are isomorphous, i.e. the dimension is an unambiguous characteristic of an isomorphism class.

Such an isomorphous transformation of two Hilbert spaces of countable dimension is obtained very simply by considering in each of them a complete orthonormal system. Thus, let u_i be the one c.o.s. in the one Hilbert space and v_i in the other, then we correlate $\sum_i u_i \alpha_i \longleftrightarrow \sum_i v_i \alpha_i$ and obtain an isomorphism of the two spaces.

A Hilbert space of countable dimension is, however, for example, also furnished by the quadratic integrable functions of a real variable in the following way: two complex-valued functions $f_1(x)$ and $f_2(x)$ for $-\infty < x < +\infty$ are called equivalent when they are the same except for a set of Lebesgue measure zero. The integral

$$\int_{-\infty}^{+\infty} |f(x)|^2 \, dx$$

is the same for equivalent functions. The equivalence classes of those functions, for which

$$\int_{-\infty}^{+\infty} |f(x)|^2 \, dx < +\infty$$

then form with the internal product

$$(f, g) = \int_{-\infty}^{+\infty} f^*(x) \, g(x) \, dx$$

a countably dimensional Hilbert space.

Another example consists of sequences of complex numbers

$$\{a_i\} \quad (i = 1, 2, \cdots \infty) \quad \text{with} \quad \sum_{i=1}^{\infty} |a_i|^2 < +\infty .$$

If we define

$$\alpha\{a_i\} + \beta\{b_i\} = \{\alpha a_i + \beta b_i\}$$

and, as internal product,

$$(\{a_i\}, \{b_i\}) = \sum_{i=1}^{\infty} a_i^* b_i ,$$

these sequences of numbers also form a countably dimensional Hilbert space.

An isomorphism between these two spaces can easily be produced by the above process: as c.o.s. $u_i(x)$ let us choose any one, e.g. the solutions given by Schrödinger for the one-dimensional harmonic oscillator. As c.o.s. in the space of the sequence $\{a_i\}$ let us choose the sequence v_k with $v_k = \{\delta_{ik}\}$, i.e. in the v_k sequence there are nothing but zeros except at the kth position, where there is a 1. With

$$f(x) = \sum_{i=1}^{\infty} \alpha_i u_i(x)$$

in which

$$\alpha_i = (u_i, f) = \int_{-\infty}^{+\infty} u_i^*(x) f(x)\, dx$$

the isomorphous correlation is given by

$$f(x) \longleftrightarrow \left\{ a_i = \int_{-\infty}^{+\infty} u_i^*(x) f(x)\, dx \right\} .$$

This isomorphism is the basis of Schrödinger's proof.

However, quantum mechanics contains still other mathematical structures: the Hermitian operators, which determine the physical structures in a manner not yet explained in a purely systematic manner. A Hermitian operator A is a linear transformation of the Hilbert space as such (in which the whole Hilbert space need not appear as a result; with unbounded operators, even the domain of definition need not be the whole Hilbert space—a mathematical problem that cannot be treated further here; the reader is referred to the mathematical literature), for which the relation $(u, Av) = (Au, v)$ holds.

If we have a c.o.s. u_i, the Au_i can be expanded in the u_i themselves:

$$Au_i = \sum_{k=1}^{\infty} u_k(u_k, Au_i) = \sum_{k=1}^{\infty} u_k a_{ki}.$$

Since $(u_k, Au_i) = (Au_k, u_i) = (u_i, Au_k)^*$, we have $a_{ki} = a_{ik}^*$.

The matrix a_{ki} determines A completely, and conversely; for when the a_{ki} are given, for any v we have

$$v = \sum_{i=1}^{\infty} u_i \alpha_i$$

$$Av = \sum_{i,k=1}^{\infty} Au_i \alpha_i = \sum_{i,k} u_k a_{ki} \alpha_i$$
$$= \sum_k u_k \left(\sum_i a_{ki} \alpha_i \right).$$

If $a_{ik} = a_{ki}^*$, A is also Hermitian, since then the relation $(u, Av) = (Au, v)$ applies generally.

In the sequence space $\{\alpha_i\}$, A is therefore given by the matrix a_{ki} with $a_{ki} = a_{ik}^*$:

$$A\{\alpha_i\} = \left\{ \sum_i a_{ki} \alpha_i \right\}.$$

In the function space of the $f(x)$, however, A can be given by other types of prescriptions, e.g.

$$Af(x) = \frac{1}{i} \frac{d}{dx} f(x).$$

It is easily shown by partial integration that $\frac{1}{i} \frac{d}{dx}$ is a Hermitian operator, since the integrated terms in the partial integration disappear because

$$\int_{-\infty}^{+\infty} |f(x)^2| \, dx$$

is finite (since $\frac{1}{i}\frac{d}{dx}$ is not bounded, in fact a more accurate treatment of the domain of definition of $\frac{1}{i}\frac{d}{dx}$ must be carried out, but again we cannot go into this here). The operator "multiply by x",

$$Af(x) = xf(x),$$

is also a Hermitian operator, as can immediately be seen.

The eigenvalue problem of a Hermitian operator

$$Au = \alpha u \tag{III.1}$$

is soluble only for real α, since using (III.1) we have

$$\alpha(u, u) = (u, Au) = (Au, u) = (u, Au)^* = \alpha^* (u, u).$$

"Eigenvectors" u_i are orthogonal for different "eigenvalues" α_i; since it follows from $Au_i = \alpha_i u_i$ that

$$(u_k, Au_i) = \alpha_i(u_k, u_i) \quad \text{and} \quad (Au_k, u_i) = \alpha_k(u_k, u_i)$$

and because $(u_k, Au_i) = (Au_k, u_i)$ finally $(\alpha_i - \alpha_k)(u_k, u_i) = 0$ and for $\alpha_i \neq \alpha_k$, therefore, $(u_k, u_i) = 0$.

If we take the simplest case that A has only discrete eigenvalues α_i and only one eigenvector u_i belongs to each α_i (i.e. more accurately, each eigenvector for a given α_i is a multiple of u_i), the u_i when they are chosen (which is in fact possible) to be normalized (i.e. $\|u_i\| = 1$) form a c.o.s. Again we cannot give the proof of this here. For the c.o.s. of the u_i, we obtain as matrix for A the diagonal matrix $a_{ik} = \alpha_i \delta_{ik}$. The formulation of a matrix in diagonal form and the solution of the eigenvalue problem are therefore equivalent problems, the first being defined only in the sequence space and the second in the abstract Hilbert space or alternatively, for example, in the function space.

An extension of the general isomorphism between the sequence space and the function space to the other structures in matrix mechanics or wave mechanics is also obtained if we assign to the matrices p_i, q_i the operators $\frac{\hbar}{i}\frac{\partial}{\partial q_i}$ and q_i and construct other operators in the same algebraic form from the

$$p_i, q_i \quad \text{or} \quad \frac{\hbar}{i}\frac{\partial}{\partial q_i}, q_i.$$

The commutation relation postulated in matrix mechanics

$$p_i q_k - q_k p_i = \frac{\hbar}{i}\delta_{ik} \tag{III.2}$$

is immediately satisfied on the wave-mechanical side because

$$\frac{\hbar}{i}\frac{\partial}{\partial q_i} q_k - q_k \frac{\hbar}{i}\frac{\partial}{\partial q_i} = \frac{\hbar}{i}\delta_{ik}. \tag{III.3}$$

When on the matrix-mechanical side there are no isomorphous solutions of (III.2) other than (III.3), matrix mechanics must be isomorphous to wave mechanics, since with the aid of a c.o.s. we obtain directly from (III.3) matrices which satisfy (III.2), as is immediately obvious from the general correlation of operators with matrices given above. The two problems of formulating $H(p, q)$ as a matrix in diagonal form and of finding the eigenvalues of $H\left(\frac{\hbar}{i}\frac{\partial}{\partial q_i}\cdots, q_1 \cdots\right)$ are, on the basis of the above discussion of the eigenvalue problem of an operator A and because of the isomorphism defined in wave mechanics by the "eigenfunctions" of H, identical. Schrödinger's arguments, briefly sketched here once again, actually still require some mathematical supplementation, as we have already indicated, but these do not change the essence of the idea.

There is no room here to develop the necessary mathematical apparatus. We shall merely briefly sketch the results (mainly without proof). For this purpose we again make use of the terminology of abstract Hilbert space.

Let us first consider the case that the so-called eigenvalue spectrum of the Hermitian operator A is not only discrete. Equation (III.1) has solutions only for the discrete eigenvalues of A. Instead of (III.1) we may also write

$$\|Au - \alpha u\| = 0. \tag{III.4}$$

Since a factor in u is arbitrary, we shall always put $\|u\| = 1$ as an auxiliary condition. The values α for which (III.4) is possible are called the discrete values of the spectrum or, in short, the discrete spectrum of A. If (under the auxiliary condition $\|u\| = 1$) it is *not* (III.4) but (Inf = lower limit)

$$\mathrm{Inf}\|Au - \alpha u\| = 0 \tag{III.5}$$

that can be achieved, α is called a continuous eigenvalue and the totality of these α is called the continuous spectrum of A. No values α for which $\mathrm{Inf}\|Au - \alpha u\| > 0$ belong to the spectrum of A.

Let us first consider once more the case of a solely discrete spectrum α_i each with "one" eigenvector u_i. Any vector v can then be expanded in the c.o.s. of the u_i:

$$v = \sum_i u_i(u_i, v).$$

The "components" $u_i(u_i, v)$ can, however, also be obtained in another manner: v is decomposed into two orthogonal parts

$$v = w + r$$

(i.e. $(w, r) = 0$). The decomposition is selected in such a way that $\|Aw - \alpha_i w\| = 0$. Thus, $w = \beta_i u_i$ and, therefore, $v = \beta_i u_i + r$ with $(r, u_i) = 0$, and consequently $\beta_i = (u_i, v)$. There are vectors v for which all components $w_i = u_i(u_i, v) \neq 0$. If such a v is selected, every other vector z can be decomposed in the following form:

$$z = \sum_i w_i \alpha_i = \sum_i \frac{w_i}{\|w_i\|} \beta_i \tag{III.6}$$

with $$\alpha_i = \frac{(w_i, z)}{\|w_i\|^2} \quad \text{and} \quad \beta_i = \frac{(w_i, z)}{\|w_i\|}.$$

For $z = v$, in particular, $\alpha_i = 1$ and $\beta_i = \|w_i\|$.

Formula (III.6) can be transferred in a certain manner to the case of a continuous spectrum: let us take a vector v, take a number ε and decompose v into orthogonal components

$$v = \sum_i w_i \quad \text{with} \quad (w_i, w_k) = 0 \quad \text{for} \quad i \neq k \qquad \text{(III.7)}$$

so that for suitable values of α_i

$$\|Aw_i - \alpha_i w_i\| \leqq \varepsilon \, \|w_i\| .$$

This expansion of v naturally depends on the choice of ε. For every other vector let us consider

$$\left\| z - \sum_i w_i \frac{(w_i, z)}{\|w_i\|^2} \right\| = \delta_z(\varepsilon). \qquad \text{(III.8)}$$

If there is a v such that $\delta_z(\varepsilon) \to 0$ for $\varepsilon \to 0$, the spectrum of A is called non-degenerate. For the case of a discrete spectrum, for $\varepsilon \to 0$ the w_i become eigenvectors of A; for the case of the continuous spectrum for $\varepsilon \neq 0$ the w_i are "quasi"-eigenvectors but tend towards zero for $\varepsilon \to 0$. In view of (III.8), however, we can regard

$$\sum_i w_i \frac{(w_i, z)}{\|w_i\|^2}$$

as an expansion in the "quasi"-eigenvectors. Now it holds generally that, for $\varepsilon \to 0$, from

$$\frac{(w_i, z)}{\|w_i\|^2} \to f(\alpha) \qquad \text{(III.9)}$$

we get a function $f(\alpha)$ belonging to the spectrum. Consequently, a function $f(\alpha)$ can be assigned to each vector z. We shall now introduce the following quantities:

$$\mu(\alpha) = \lim_{\varepsilon \to 0} \left\| \sum_{\substack{i \\ (\alpha_i \leqq \alpha)}} w_i \right\|^2 = \lim_{\varepsilon \to 0} \sum_{\substack{i \\ (\alpha_i \leqq \alpha)}} \|w_i\|^2 . \qquad \text{(III.10)}$$

Then for two vectors:

$$(z, y) = \lim_{\varepsilon \to 0} \sum_i \frac{(w_i, z)^*}{\|w_i\|^2} \frac{(w_i, y)}{\|w_i\|^2} \|w_i\|^2$$

$$= \int f^*(\alpha) \, g(\alpha) \, d\mu(\alpha) \qquad \text{(III.11)}$$

with $f(\alpha)$ from (III.9) and a corresponding formula for y and $g(\alpha)$. Consequently the correlation

$$z \longleftrightarrow f(\alpha) \tag{III.12}$$

has become an isomorphism between the abstract Hilbert space and the function space. According to (III.10) $\mu(\alpha)$ has a discontinuity at the positions of the discrete spectrum and increases continuously at the positions of the continuous spectrum. Formula (III.11) is therefore to be defined exactly like a Lebesgue–Stieltjes integral. The discontinuities can be separated off as a sum:

$$\int f^*(\alpha)\, g(\alpha)\, d\mu(\alpha) = \sum_i f^*(\alpha_i)\, g(\alpha_i)\, \mu_s(\alpha_i) + \int f^*(\alpha)\, g(\alpha)\, d\nu(\alpha), \tag{III.13}$$

in which the sum must extend over the discrete eigenvalues α_i (with $\mu_s(\alpha_i)$ = the jump in $\mu(\alpha)$ at the point α_i); in addition, in the integral we must put

$$\nu(\alpha) = \mu(\alpha) - \sum_{\substack{i \\ (\alpha_i \leqq \alpha)}} \mu_s(\alpha_i).$$

When $d\nu(\alpha)/d\alpha$ exists (which is always the situation in physical cases) the correlation (III.12) can be replaced by a "normalized" one:

$$z \longleftrightarrow \mathscr{F}(\alpha) \tag{III.14}$$

with

$$\mathscr{F}(\alpha_i) = f(\alpha_i)\, \mu_s(\alpha_i)^{1/2}$$

for the discrete eigenvalues α_i and

$$\mathscr{F}(\alpha) = f(\alpha) \left(\frac{d\nu}{d\alpha}\right)^{1/2}$$

for the continuous spectrum. Then, we obtain instead of (III.11), (III.13):

$$(z, y) = \sum_i \mathscr{F}^*(\alpha_i)\, \mathscr{G}(\alpha_i) + \int \mathscr{F}^*(\alpha)\, \mathscr{G}(\alpha)\, d\alpha. \tag{III.15}$$

The correlation (III.14) forms an isomorphous mapping $\mathscr{H} \longleftrightarrow \mathscr{R}$ from $\mathscr{H}$ onto the $\mathscr{R}$ space of the functions $\mathscr{F}(\alpha)$, a mapping which is adapted to the operator A, since for the operator A

$$Az \longleftrightarrow \alpha\mathscr{F}(\alpha), \tag{III.16}$$

as readily follows from (III.8) because

$$\|Aw_i - \alpha_i w_i\| \leqq \varepsilon \, \|w_i\| .$$

Consequently, we call $\mathscr{R}$ an A-representation.

Hence, because of (III.16), the Schrödinger functions $\varphi(x)$ are nothing other than the representation of the Hilbert space corresponding to the position operator and matrix mechanics is nothing other than the representation corresponding to the Hamiltonian operator (if this has a discrete non-degenerate spectrum as in the case of the harmonic oscillator); the Schrödinger transformation of wave mechanics to matrix mechanics is the isomorphous correlation of the two representations.

One of the most important techniques of calculation in the Hilbert space consists in selecting a suitable representation according to the problem and passing from one to another in the way that Schrödinger has shown for the transition from the coordinate to the energy representation. For an exhaustive treatment of this technique, the reader must be referred to the special textbook literature.

Here we shall only go briefly into the still remaining case in which the spectrum of A is degenerate:

In this case, it is most convenient to select a system of commuting operators in such a way that their common spectrum is no longer degenerate. If, for example, A and B are two commuting Hermitian operators, i.e. $AB = BA$, it follows from

$$Aw - \alpha w = 0,$$

that

$$ABw - \alpha Bw = B(Aw - \alpha w) = 0,$$

i.e. that Bw is also an eigenvector for the eigenvalue α.

All eigenvectors for the eigenvalue α of A form a sub-space which in the case of a degenerate eigenvalue is more than one-dimensional. In this so-called eigenspace of A for the eigenvalue α, the vectors can still be chosen in such a way that they are also eigenvectors of B. A system of commuting operators has a non-degenerate spectrum if one-dimensional eigenspaces are determined by the specification of all eigenvalues of the operators. For example, if A and B form such a system, the common spectrum α, β of A, B can be regarded as a two-dimensional set of points and the vectors of the Hilbert space can be represented by functions $f(\alpha, \beta)$ over this common spectrum.

The three position operators q_1, q_2, q_3 of an electron, for example, form such a system of commuting operators the spectrum of which is given by the x_1, x_2, x_3 so that the vectors of the Hilbert space can be represented by the Schrödinger wave functions $\varphi(x_1 x_2 x_3)$.

But the three momentum operators p_1, p_2, and p_3 also form such a system. How can we pass from the "coordinate representation" to the "momentum representation"? For this purpose in accordance to what has been said above we must seek the (quasi)-eigenfunctions of the momentum operators. We do this in the coordinate representation where the momentum operators are given by $\frac{\hbar}{i}\frac{\partial}{\partial x_1}$, $\frac{\hbar}{i}\frac{\partial}{\partial x_2}$, and $\frac{\hbar}{i}\frac{\partial}{\partial x_3}$. The three equations

$$\frac{\hbar}{i}\frac{\partial}{\partial x_k}\varphi(x_1 x_2 x_3) = p_k \varphi(x_1 x_2 x_3)$$

have as their common solution

$$\varphi = e^{\frac{i}{\hbar}\sum_{k=1}^{3} p_k x_k}.$$

However, these functions are not vectors in the Hilbert space, since $\int |\varphi^2|\, dx_1\, dx_2\, dx_3$ does not exist. However, wave packets with an arbitrarily small range in the p_1, p_2, p_3 space

$$\chi_{p_1 p_2 p_3}(x_1 x_2 x_3) = \int_{p_1-\varepsilon}^{p_1+\varepsilon} dp_1' \int_{p_2-\varepsilon}^{p_2+\varepsilon} dp_2' \int_{p_3-\varepsilon}^{p_3+\varepsilon} dp_3'\, e^{\frac{i}{\hbar}\sum_{k=1}^{3} p_k' x_k}$$

are vectors in the Hilbert space with

$$\left\| \frac{\hbar}{i} \frac{\partial}{\partial x_k} \chi_{p_1p_2p_3} - p_k\chi_{p_1p_2p_3} \right\|^2$$

$$= \int \left| \frac{\hbar}{i} \frac{\partial}{\partial x_k} \chi_{p_1p_2p_3} - p_k\chi_{p_1p_2p_3} \right|^2 dx_1\, dx_2\, dx_3 \leqq 8\varepsilon^5 .$$

The $\chi_{p_1p_2p_3}$ are therefore "quasi"-eigenvectors. With

$$\eta(p_1p_2p_3) = \frac{1}{h^3} \int e^{\frac{i}{\hbar}\sum_{k=1}^{3} p_kx_k} \psi(x_1x_2x_3)\, dx_1\, dx_2\, dx_3$$

we then obtain the representant $\eta\,(p_1p_2p_3)$ in momentum space of the vector with the representant $\psi(x_1x_2x_3)$ in coordinate space. The normalization is so arranged that

$$\int |\psi|^2\, dx_1\, dx_2\, dx_3 = 1 \quad \text{gives} \quad \int |\eta|^2\, dp_1\, dp_2\, dp_3 = 1 .$$

Because

$$\frac{1}{h^3} \int e^{\frac{i}{\hbar}\sum_{l=1}^{3} p_lx_l} \frac{\hbar}{i} \frac{\partial}{\partial x_k} \psi(x_1x_2x_3)\, dx_1\, dx_2\, dx_3 = p_k\eta(p_1p_2p_3)$$

the momentum operators assume the expected form "multiplication by p_k" and because

$$\frac{1}{h^3} \int e^{\frac{i}{\hbar}\sum_{l=1}^{3} p_lx_l} x_k\psi(x_1x_2x_3)\, dx_1\, dx_2\, dx_3 = -\frac{\hbar}{i} \frac{\partial}{\partial p_k} \eta(p_1p_2p_3)$$

the coordinate operators assume the form $-\dfrac{\hbar}{i}\dfrac{\partial}{\partial p_k}$.

After we have in this way, on the basis of Schrödinger's ideas, obtained an insight into the various "possibilities of representation" of quantum mechanics, the question of the connection of the time dependence in matrix and wave mechanics still remains somewhat obscure. The two forms (II.46) and (II.63) are at least not immediately identical. Before we clarify this question, we shall go into the problem of the physical interpretation.

CHAPTER IV

The Physical Interpretation of Quantum Mechanics

AFTER the mathematical system of quantum mechanics had taken shape, there was still no systematic method of correlation between mathematical objects and physical processes such as we postulated in Chapter I under (3). It is true that here and there in the papers by Heisenberg and Schrödinger isolated connections between mathematically calculated quantities and physically measured quantities were formulated, otherwise it would not have been possible to guess at a theory; however, the papers sketched above do not go beyond guessing the physical interpretation for individual cases. We shall now on the basis of these papers summarize these individual links between physics and mathematics.

In Heisenberg's paper it is the spectral frequencies $\omega_{nm} = \frac{1}{\hbar}(E_n - E_m)$, the energy levels E_n and the transition probabilities from E_n to E_m in the emission of a light quantum (to be calculated from the "matrix elements" q_{nm}) that are to be compared with experience.

Schrödinger also desires first to elucidate the transition frequencies and energy levels. For this purpose Schrödinger first attempts to interpret a "mass point" as a wave packet, i.e. he regards the approximate position and the approximate velocity of a wave packet as representing the position and velocity of a particle. However, it would be the wave and not the particle that was real; but wave of what?

In § 5 of his paper on the relationship of matrix to wave mechanics, Schrödinger attempts to say something more about the wave. He seeks an expression for a continuous charge and current density that would give a purely classical electromagnetic field. In this paper he still does not find the "correct" expressions but first puts $\psi \frac{\partial \psi^*}{\partial t}$ as charge density. In connection with these considerations, he then attempts finally in the fourth communication to give the wave function a physical interpretation: $\psi\psi^*$ is then interpreted as the expression for the charge density. But then, in order to be able to treat the case of "several" particles, the expression "weight function" for $\psi\psi^*$, from which the "charge density" of one of the n particles is obtained only by integration over $n - 1$ particles, appears. Using this correct expression for the charge density, an expression for the current density is also obtained. But it remains the case, in spite of the use of the expression "weight function", that the expressions obtained are regarded as the correct continuous charge and current densities. The fact that in an eigenvibration the charge density is constant with time and the current density is zero is regarded as an advantage, since it explains the "non-radiativity" of these states of eigenvibration with the discrete energies E_n. However, this is precisely in contrast to the experience that all higher energy states other than the ground state radiate energy "spontaneously", i.e. by themselves, and pass into lower states and this *on an average just as fast* as classical orbits would radiate energy. This circumstance may be the first to awaken scepsis with respect to the proposed interpretation, although, of course, in view of its success in relation to the dispersion theory represented by it there must be "something correct" in it. The decisive step to the final elucidation of the physical interpretation was then given by Born in his paper on the quantum mechanics of collision processes.

It would again be outside the scope of this book if we were to go here into the modern theory of scattering and the importance of Born's paper for it. This paper itself may therefore serve as an introduction to this field.

Here, rather, we shall merely use the interpretation of the

mathematical system of quantum mechanics proposed in this paper of Born's, which has proved to be the "correct" explanation, and discuss those problems which this explanation has raised and is still raising today.

Recognizing the inadequacies of the previous interpretations (which have just been sketched), Born suggested that: the ψ-function determines the "probability" of the motion of the corpuscles—i.e., for example, of their position and momentum. A wave packet is not to be regarded as an approximation to a corpuscle, so that the corpuscles are *in fact* more or less extended *waves*, but the ψ-wave determines only the probability, for example, of the position of the corpuscles which, themselves, have (practically as good as) no extension.

The decisive turning point in the interpretation consists in the use of the concept of probability. Without going at once into the question that this immediately raises of what this probability actually is, we shall consider the mathematical expressions which give this probability; they must in some way be capable of being calculated from the ψ-wave.

First, Born considers the expansion of the Hilbert space vector ψ with the normalization $\|\psi\| = 1$ in the eigenvectors of the energy operator H:

$$H\psi_n = E_n\psi_n, \ \|\psi_n\| = 1$$

and

$$\psi = \sum_n c_n \psi.$$

Because

$$\|\psi\|^2 = 1 \quad \text{and} \quad (\psi_n, \psi_m) = \delta_{nm},$$

$$1 = \|\psi\|^2 = \sum_n |c_n|^2, \tag{IV.1}$$

The explanation is as follows: $|c_n|^2$ is the probability for the energy value E_n. Formula (IV.1) then expresses nothing other than the fact that the sum of all probabilities is equal to 1.

If we now calculate $(\psi, H\psi)$ we obtain

$$(\psi, H\psi) = \left(\sum_n c_n\psi_n, H \sum_m c_m\psi_m\right)$$

$$= \left(\sum_n c_n\psi_n, \sum_m c_m E_m\psi_m\right) = \sum_n E_n|c_n|^2. \tag{IV.2}$$

The expression $\sum_n E_n |c_n|^2$ is then, however, the energy averaged with the probabilities $|c_n|^2$, the so-called "expectation value" of the energy.

The same arguments will be used for the case of the "momentum operator". If, for simplicity, we consider the one-dimensional case:

$$p\varphi_k(x) = \frac{\hbar}{i}\frac{d}{dx}\varphi_k(x) = \hbar k \varphi_k(x)$$

has as solutions the "improper" eigenfunctions

$$\varphi_k(x) = \frac{1}{(2\pi)^{1/2}} e^{ikx},$$

from which, for ε as small as may be desired, using

$$\int_{k-\varepsilon}^{k+\varepsilon} \varphi_{k'}(x)\, dk'$$

we obtain "quasi-eigenfunctions" for the value $\hbar k$ of the spectrum of the momentum operator. Each vector $\psi(x)$ can be expanded in the $\varphi_k(x)$:

$$\psi(x) = \frac{1}{(2\pi)^{1/2}} \int_{-\infty}^{+\infty} c(k)\, e^{ikx}\, dk. \tag{IV.3}$$

From $\|\psi\|^2 = 1$ it then follows that

$$\|\psi\|^2 = \int |\psi|^2\, dx = \int |c(k)|^2\, dk = 1. \tag{IV.4}$$

The physical interpretation is as follows: $|c(k)|^2\, dk$ is the probability that the momentum (measured in units $\hbar$) has a value between k and $k + dk$. Formula (IV.4) is again the expression of the fact that the sum of all probabilities is 1. Furthermore, we obtain

$$(\psi, p\psi) = \int \psi^*(x) \frac{\hbar}{i}\frac{d}{dx}\psi(x)\, dx$$

$$= \frac{1}{(2\pi)^{1/2}} \int \psi^*(x) \int \hbar k c(k)\, e^{ikx}\, dk\, dx = \int \hbar k |c(k)|^2\, dk,$$

i.e. the expression $(\psi, p\psi)$ for the expectation value of the momentum.

This explanation made on the basis of individual examples can, however, very easily be formulated more generally. Before we do this, we shall first seek a formula for the positional probability. It is an obvious matter to interpret $|\psi(x)|^2\, dx$ itself as the probability that the position of a particle is between x and $x + dx$. Since

$$\|\psi\|^2 = \int |\psi|^2\, dx = 1$$

the sum of the probabilities is again equal to 1, and since

$$(\psi, q\psi) = \int \psi^*(x)\, x\psi(x)\, dx = \int x|\psi|^2\, dx$$

the expectation value for the position is $(\psi, q\psi)$.

Thus we come to the following interpretation: quantum mechanics assigns Hermitian operators to measurable quantities (the observables). If A is such an operator, we shall also designate the measurable quantities by A. The expectation value of A must then be calculated from the vector ψ in accordance with

$$M(A) = (\psi, A\psi). \tag{IV.5}$$

The possible measured values of A are those of the spectrum of A. The probability for these measured values can also be calculated from equation (IV.5) if a suitable operator is introduced into this for A which gives the "measured value" 1 only when the measured values of A are in the desired interval and the "measured value" 0 when the measured values of A are outside this interval. We shall first explain this further on the basis of the above examples:

For the case of a non-degenerate discrete spectrum of H, we introduce with

$$\psi = \sum_n c_n \psi_n$$

the family of projection operators P_E by means of

$$P_E \psi = \sum_{\substack{n \\ (E_n \leq E)}} c_n \psi_n. \tag{IV.6}$$

Then $P_{-\infty} = 0$, $P_{+\infty} = 1$. P_E projects the vector ψ perpendicular onto the sub-space that is fixed by all the eigenvectors ψ for which the eigenvalues $E_n \leqq E$. Since $H\psi = \sum_n c_n E_n \psi_n$ we may write

$$H\psi = \int E\, dP_E \psi \tag{IV.7}$$

the integral being defined as a Stieltjes integral. Formula (IV.7) can also be written in shortened form

$$H = \int E\, dP_E. \tag{IV.8}$$

We immediately obtain

$$(\psi, (P_E - P_{E'})\psi) = \sum_{\substack{n \\ (E' < E_n \leqq E)}} |c_n|^2, \tag{IV.9}$$

i.e. the probability that the measured value ε of the energy H falls in the interval $E' < \varepsilon \leqq E$ is equal to

$$M(P_E - P_{E'}) = (\psi, (P_E - P_{E'})\psi). \tag{IV.10}$$

$P_E - P_{E'}$ is the projection operator on the sub-space that is fixed by all eigenvectors and eigenvalues E_n from the interval $E' < E_n \leqq E$. This projection operator, which commutes with H, itself has the eigenvalues 1 for all eigenvectors ψ_n with $E' < E_n \leqq E$, and 0 for all other ψ_n.

This representation can also be transferred to the momentum operator $\dfrac{\hbar}{i}\dfrac{d}{dx}$. The sub-space fixed by all "quasi-eigenvectors" to the spectral values $p \leqq \hbar k$ is given by all the vectors $\chi(x)$, the Fourier expansion of which has the form

$$\chi(x) = \frac{1}{(2\pi)^{1/2}} \int_{-\infty}^{k} \gamma(k')\, e^{ik'x}\, dk'.$$

Consequently, we define the projection operator E_k which when applied to $\psi(x)$ in accordance with (IV.3) gives

$$E_k\psi(x) = \frac{1}{(2\pi)^{1/2}} \int_{-\infty}^{k} c(k')\, e^{ik'x}\, dk'. \tag{IV.11}$$

Then, in a similar manner to (IV.7), we have:

$$\frac{\hbar}{i}\frac{d}{dx} = \int \hbar k \, dE_k; \qquad \text{(IV.12)}$$

and the probability that the measured value p of the momentum falls in the interval $\hbar k' < p \leqq \hbar k$ is

$$M(E_k - E_{k'}) = (\psi, (E_k - E_{k'})\,\psi) = \int_{k'}^{k} |c(k'')|^2 \, dk''. \qquad \text{(IV.13)}$$

The matter is particularly simple for the position operator. With

$$F_{x'}\psi(x) = \begin{cases} \psi(x) & \text{for} \quad x \leqq x' \\ 0 & \text{for} \quad x > x' \end{cases} \qquad \text{(IV.14)}$$

$F_{x'}$, is a projection operator with

$$q\psi(x) = x\psi(x) = \int x' \, dF_{x'}\psi(x'), \qquad \text{(IV.14a)}$$

i.e.

$$q = \int x' \, dF_{x'},$$

The probability that the measured value x of the position falls in the interval $x' < x \leqq x''$ is then

$$M(F_{x''} - F_{x'}) = (\psi, (F_{x''} - F_{x'})\,\psi) = \int_{x'}^{x''} |\psi(x''')|^2 \, dx'''. \qquad \text{(IV.15)}$$

We summarize as follows: for each Hermitian operator A there is a family of projection operators E_α (the so-called spectral family) with $E_{+\infty} = 1$, $E_{-\infty} = 0$, in which E_α projects on to the sub-space fixed by all the eigenvectors (or quasi-eigenvectors) of A with values of the spectrum $\leqq \alpha$. Then the spectral resolution

$$A = \int_{-\infty}^{+\infty} \alpha \, dE_\alpha \qquad \text{(IV.16)}$$

applies. The probability that the measured value α of the observable A falls in the interval $\alpha' < \alpha \leqq \alpha''$ is

$$M(E_{\alpha''} - E_{\alpha'}) = (\psi, (E_{\alpha''} - E_{\alpha'})\,\psi). \qquad \text{(IV.17)}$$

According to the definition of the expectation value, the expectation value of A is equal to the integral

$$\int_{-\infty}^{+\infty} \alpha \, dM(E_\alpha),$$

since $dM(E_\alpha)$ is the probability that the measured value α lies in the interval α to $\alpha + d\alpha$. In view of (IV.16), therefore, the expectation value of A becomes

$$M(A) = (\psi, A\psi). \tag{IV.18}$$

Formula (IV.18) is therefore a consequence of (IV.17). Consequently, (IV.17) must be regarded as the basic formula for the calculation of probabilities.

Formula (IV.17) becomes particularly simple when we pass to the representation of the Hilbert space correlated with the operator A. In this representation the vectors of the Hilbert space are given by functions $\psi(\alpha, \beta, \cdots)$ over the spectrum α of A and $\beta, \cdots$ of other operators $B, \cdots$ commuting with A (if the spectrum of A is degenerate) under which conditions the operator A itself then assumes the simple form "multiplication by α" so that $E_{\alpha'}$ assumes the simple form

$$E_{\alpha'}\psi(\alpha, \beta, \cdots) = \begin{cases} \psi(\alpha, \beta, \cdots) & \text{for } \alpha \leqq \alpha' \\ 0 & \text{for } \alpha > \alpha'. \end{cases}$$

Then, from (IV.17)

$$M(E_{\alpha''} - E_{\alpha'}) = \sum_{\substack{\alpha_n \\ (\alpha' < \alpha_n \leqq \alpha'')}} \int |\psi(\alpha_n, \beta, \cdots)|^2 d\beta \cdots$$

$$+ \int_{\alpha'}^{\alpha''} d\alpha \int_{-\infty}^{+\infty} d\beta \int \cdots |\psi(\alpha, \beta, \cdots)|^2, \tag{IV.19}$$

in which the summation must be carried out over the discrete eigenvalues α_n and the integration over the continuous spectrum. $\int d\beta$ will symbolically also contain possible summations over discrete eigenvalues β_m. Formula (IV.15) is thus only a special case of (IV.19) for the case of the coordinate representation.

If in (IV.17) we write P for short for the projection operator $E_{\alpha''} - E_{\alpha'}$, we have the fundamental statement:

$$\boxed{\text{the probability for } P = M(P) = (\psi, P\psi).} \qquad \text{(IV.20)}$$

Formula (IV.20) is a short summary of Born's statistical interpretation of quantum mechanics.

Each vector ψ can be resolved into the two mutually orthogonal parts $P\psi$ and $(1 - P)\psi$:

$$\varphi = P\varphi + (1 - P)\varphi.$$

Since $P\psi$ is already in the sub-space projected on to by P, $PP\psi = P\psi$, i.e. $P^2 = P$. It follows from

$$\varphi = P\varphi + (1 - P)\varphi$$

and $(1 - P)\varphi$ orthogonal to $P\psi$ that

$$(\varphi, P\psi) = (P\varphi, P\psi) = (P\varphi, \psi);$$

and, therefore, in particular from (IV.20)

$$M(P) = \|P\psi\|^2. \qquad \text{(IV.21)}$$

P has as eigenvalues, i.e. measured values, only the values 1 for all vectors from the sub-space projected on to by P, and 0 for all vectors perpendicular to this sub-space, for we have

$$P(P\psi) = P\psi \quad \text{and} \quad P(1 - P)\varphi = 0.$$

According to (IV.20) the probability for P and the expectation value of P are identical, which is also the same thing according to our ideas, since by the definition of the expectation value the expectation value of a quantity with the possible values 1 or 0 is equal to the probability of the value 1.

Although the explanation given by (IV.20) has proved to be physically correct, it must not be concealed that some questions still remain open. The first question is: what projection operators are assigned to the various possible questions, i.e. the various possible "1 or 0" measurements? It appears at first sight as if we already had an answer to this. Let us seek for the observable A

the spectral family E_α in accordance with (IV.16); then we have to put for the observable P (measured value of P equal to 1 when the measured value α of A is in the interval $\alpha' < \alpha \leqq \alpha''$, and measured value of P equal to 0 when α is outside this interval) $P = E_{\alpha''} - E_{\alpha'}$. However, this is no solution but merely a restatement of the problem, since the question then arises as to which operators A are to be assigned to just which measurable quantities. However, the family E_α characterizes A completely, and conversely. Since "scales of measurement" are arbitrary, we can justifiably take the standpoint that the projection operators represent the more fundamental structure and that from a suitable family of projection operators E with the help of a selectable parameter α we then *define* first the scale of measurement and thereby A in accordance with (IV.16).

The second question that arises is that of the significance of ψ itself. ψ is the quantity which actually determines the probabilities for the various P according to (IV.20); but which ψ is to be selected in a concrete case? This second question is closely connected, or is practically identical, with the question: what is probability? For ψ is just that which probability determines.

Let us therefore first turn to the question of what is probability. Although much has been and can be written on this point, in physical theory it reduces in the first place to what probability means as a determinable fact within the directly obtained measured effects obtained by the experimental physicist. Again, Born gives an answer to this, even if it is not expressed in such a clear form: he calls the probability $|c_n|^2$ the frequency with which the energy values E_n occur "in an assembly of identical, uncoupled, atoms" (p. 209). Probability is therefore frequency of measured results even if this is not formulated quite so explicitly by Born. He speaks of the frequency of the states ψ_n instead of the frequency of the measured values E_n. But by the use of the word "state" ψ_n is meant: state with the energy E_n. However, from the purely logical point of view, there is still a difference between the state of an atom with the energy E_n and the measured value of the energy for an atom with the result E_n.

In the "physical" end-effect, however, the term "state with the energy E_n" means, in the final account, only that a measurement of the energy gives the result E_n. It cannot be wondered at that the terminology of the first papers still makes use without reflection of a manner of speaking which equates the measured result with the determination of a property present in an object. However, if we defer the consideration of this obscurity which is still present, one thing has been made abundantly clear—that physical probability is equivalent to frequency, frequency in a "assembly of identical, uncoupled, atoms", a frequency which can be measured, i.e. determined, just in this "assembly".

In this situation it is not quite clear what the word "identical" atoms is supposed to signify; we shall interpret it in such a way that it will mean *only* that we have nothing but hydrogen atoms or nothing but nitrogen atoms, i.e. identical atoms in this sense. "Identical" objects are therefore objects of the same "kind". Only for objects of the same kind can "*a*" quantum mechanics be written; objects of another type require another quantum mechanics.

This raises two questions: what is a definite "kind" of objects, and what is an "assembly of such uncoupled systems of the same kind"? The "kind" of objects is characterized by certain unchangeable properties that can be determined experimentally (at least under certain conditions, i.e. in a large class of experiments). Thus, for example, an electron is characterized by its mass and charge, and a hydrogen atom by its construction from one proton and one electron. The experimental determination of the kind of objects therefore *precedes* the use of quantum mechanics to elucidate the experiments on objects of just this particular kind. This short and not exhaustive analysis of the term "identical objects", i.e. objects of the "same kind", may suffice. Only the physics of the elementary particles makes the term "kind" quite clear physically in its significance and in its restrictedness.

Consequently, in the analysis of the interpretation of quantum mechanics below we always restrict ourselves to a single kind of objects, so that it may be permitted for the sake of brevity to speak simply of the objects. Probability is therefore frequency in an assembly of non-coupled objects. This assembly of non-coupled objects is often called for short "ensemble". The physical interpretation of quantum mechanics is therefore produced by a connection not with an individual result of measurement but with the frequency of the results of measurements on a population. This does not mean the frequency of an "ensemble" of only a few objects, since it is found experimentally that a frequency relating to few objects is subject to marked variations when the same experiment is repeated, while this frequency assumes the same value almost always even with repeated experiments when the "ensemble" consists of "very many" objects. The variations of the frequencies when the experiment is repeated becomes smaller and smaller with an increase in number of objects in the "ensemble". We shall speak of "ensembles" only in this last sense below, in fact of those "ensembles" in which because of the very large number the exact number of objects is no longer of significance.

This also makes clearer what the word "non-coupled" systems means: the experiment is to be arranged in such a way that no interaction between objects of the "ensemble" is possible, which is asssured experimentally with the greatest certainty if the individual objects of the "ensemble" are investigated successively after sufficiently large intervals of time.

It is in fact a direct consequence of the ideas that have just been sketched of the experimentally testable concept of probability as frequency within an "ensemble" to regard the Hilbert space factor ψ in (IV.21) as representing the "ensemble", i.e. the assembly of objects.

But right from the beginning, on the basis of the eigenvectors ψ_n of the energy operator H for the eigenvalue E_n the word "state" has become accepted for the energy E_n and therefore, in general, the term "state" for the vector ψ in the Hilbert space. Formula (IV.21) is then interpreted as the probability of the fact that an object in the "state" ψ has the "property" P. This sentence is a short and therefore very *practical* formulation of the content of (IV.21) but at first sight blurs its meaning, so that it is not clear without further analysis what is to be understood by "state" and "property". If, on the other hand, the words "probability of the property P in the state ψ" are regarded only as a shortened formulation of "frequency" with which, in measurement by means of a "yes–no apparatus" symbolized by P, the "yes effect" occurs in the ensemble characterized by ψ, the short formulation given above is a legitimate means of communicating physical statements.

However, it is now seen that the vectors ψ of the Hilbert space are not alone sufficiently general to characterize the physically possible ensembles. If, for example, we have the two ensembles ψ_1 and ψ_2, a third ensemble can easily be obtained experimentally by "mixing": N_1 objects are taken from the first ensemble and N_2 from the second, and they are mixed to give the new ensemble consisting of $N = N_1 + N_2$ objects. Here, as always, N_1 and N_2 are very large numbers. The frequency h for any "yes–no" measurement in the mixed ensemble is therefore

$$h = \frac{N_1}{N} h_1 + \frac{N_2}{N} h_2$$

with the frequencies h_1 and h_2 within the ensembles ψ_1 and ψ_2. The number $\lambda = \frac{N_1}{N}$ may assume practically all values between 0 and 1, since N_1 and N_2 are very large. According to (IV.21), therefore, for the mixed ensemble we have the probability function $M(P)$ with

$$M(P) = \lambda M_1(P) + (1 - \lambda)\, M_2(P) = \lambda \|P\psi_1\|^2 + (1 - \lambda)\, \|P\psi_2\|^2. \tag{IV.22}$$

However, this $M(P)$ cannot (unless $\psi_1 = e^{i\alpha}\psi_2$) be written in the form $\|P\psi\|^2$. Consequently, we seek a mathematical formulation for (IV.21) in which the symbol for the ensemble occurs not in quadratic form but in linear form, since we can then easily formulate (IV.22). This is possible with the aid of the concept of the trace of an operator. This is defined by

$$\mathrm{Tr}(A) = \sum_{\nu} (\varphi_\nu, A\varphi_\nu),$$

in which the φ_ν are a c.o.s. If ψ_ν is another c.o.s., by means of the expansions

$$\varphi_\nu = \sum_{\mu} \psi_\mu (\psi_\mu, \varphi_\nu),$$

$$\psi_\mu = \sum_{\nu} \varphi_\nu (\varphi_\nu, \psi_\mu) = \sum_{\nu} \varphi_\nu (\psi_\mu, \varphi_\nu)^*,$$

it follows that

$$\mathrm{Tr}(A) = \sum_{\nu\mu} (\varphi_\nu, A\psi_\mu)(\psi_\mu, \varphi_\nu)$$

$$= \sum_{\mu} \Big(\sum_{\nu} \varphi_\nu (\psi_\mu, \varphi_\nu)^*, A\psi_\mu \Big) = \sum_{\mu} (\psi_\mu, A\psi_\mu).$$

The value of the trace is therefore independent of the c.o.s. Considering the projection operator P_ψ onto the vector $\psi (P_\psi \psi = \psi(\psi, \psi)$, if $\|\psi\| = 1)$ we have, since $P^2 = P$,

$$\|P\psi\|^2 = (\psi, P\psi) = \sum_{\nu} (\psi_\nu, PP_\psi \psi_\nu) = \mathrm{Tr}(PP_\psi),$$

which can easily be proven if the c.o.s. is chosen in such a way that $\psi_1 = \psi$. (IV.21) can therefore be written also in the form

$$M(P) = \mathrm{Tr}(PP_\psi). \tag{IV.23}$$

Since Tr(A) is linear in A according to definition, it immediately follows from (IV.22) that

$$M(P) = \mathrm{Tr}\big(P(\lambda P_{\psi_1} + (1 - \lambda) P_{\psi_2})\big),$$

i.e.

$$M(P) = \mathrm{Tr}(PW) \tag{IV.24}$$

with $W = \lambda P_{\psi_1} + (1 - \lambda) P_{\psi_2}$. This W is a Hermitian operator, since the P_{ψ_1}, P_{ψ_2} are Hermitian operators and λ is real. W is positive (semi-) definite, i.e. for all vectors φ:

$$(\varphi, W\varphi) \geqq 0 \tag{IV.25}$$

(IV.25) follows from the fact that P_ψ is positive definite (since $(\psi, P_\psi\varphi) = |(\varphi, \psi)|^2$) and λ like $(1 - \lambda)$ is positive. Furthermore, $\mathrm{Tr}\, W = 1$.

For any two positive definite Hermitian operators W_1 and W_2 with $\mathrm{Tr}\, W_1 = 1, \mathrm{Tr}\, W_2 = 1$, the "mixed" operator $W = \lambda W_1 + (1 - \lambda) W_2$ is again a Hermitian operator. On the other hand, a positive definite Hermitian operator W with $\mathrm{Tr}\, W = 1$ can have only discrete eigenvalues w_ν (with $0 \leqq w_\nu \leqq 1$ and $\sum_\nu w_\nu = 1$), which will not be proved here. If ψ_ν are the eigenvectors for the eigenvalues w_ν, W can be written in the form

$$W = \sum_\nu w_\nu P_{\psi_\nu},$$

i.e. interpreted as a "mixture" of the P_{ψ_ν} with the weights w_ν.

This gives us the general interpretation of quantum mechanics: in accordance with (IV.24) the ensembles are assigned to the positive definite Hermitian operators W with $\mathrm{Tr}\, W = 1$, the Yes–No measurements to the projection operators P, and the expression $M(P)$ to the frequency of P in W. In extension of (IV.18), the mean of an observable A in the ensemble W is then

$$M(A) = \mathrm{Tr}(AW) \tag{IV.26}$$

which, however, in fact, does not go beyond (IV.24), since in view of (IV.16)

$$\begin{aligned} M(A) &= \int \alpha \, dM(E_\alpha) = \int \alpha \, d\,\mathrm{Tr}(E_\alpha W) \\ &= \mathrm{Tr}\Big(\int \alpha \, dE_\alpha W\Big) = \mathrm{Tr}(AW). \end{aligned}$$

The question arises as to whether the positive definite Hermitian operators W with $\mathrm{Tr}\, W = 1$ are sufficiently general to be able to characterize all possible ensembles, i.e. are there other expressions $M(P)$ besides (IV.24). For this purpose, of course, a requirement must be placed on this $M(P)$. To understand this requirement it is necessary to go somewhat more deeply into the problem of the correlation of the projection operators with the Yes–No measurements. On the basis of the resolution of a Hermitian operator into its spectral resolution, we set up the following postulate for this correlation:

(α) Orthogonal projection operators (i.e. projection operators to orthogonal sub-spaces) are assigned to exclusive, but combinable Yes–No measurements.

If, in fact, for example, $E_{\alpha_1} - E_{\alpha_2}$ and $E_{\alpha_3} - E_{\alpha_4}$ are the projection operators for the Yes–No measurements that the measured values of the magnitude A fall in the intervals $\alpha_2, \cdots, \alpha_1$ and $\alpha_4, \cdots, \alpha_3$, respectively, and these two intervals are disjoint, $E_{\alpha_1} - E_{\alpha_2}$ and $E_{\alpha_3} - E_{\alpha_4}$ are orthogonal to one another. Both Yes–No measurements are measurable together, but two "Yes" can never coincide. Furthermore, $(E_{\alpha_1} - E_{\alpha_2}) + (E_{\alpha_3} - E_{\alpha_4})$ is the projection operator for the Yes–No measurement that the measured values of A fall within *one* of the two intervals $\alpha_2, \cdots, \alpha_1$ and $\alpha_4, \cdots, \alpha_3$, so that $M(E_{\alpha_1} - E_{\alpha_2}) + M(E_{\alpha_3} - E_{\alpha_4})$ must hold for the frequency.

We summarize this intuitive relationship by means of the further postulates:

(β) If P_i are mutually orthogonal projection operators, the following Yes–No measurement is correlated with $P = \sum_i P_i$: the measured value of P is exactly equal to 1 (i.e. Yes) when it is equal to 1 for any one of the P_i.

Because of (α), several P_i can never combine to give the measured value 1 together, but it must always be one of the P_i at the most. It therefore follows from (α) and (β) that for mutually orthogonal P_i the following relation must hold

$$M\left(\sum_i P_i\right) = \sum_i M(P_i). \tag{IV.27}$$

Since the operator 1 represents the Yes–No measurement with "always Yes" (the operator 1 has only the eigenvalue 1), we require as normalization:

$$M(1) = 1. \tag{IV.28}$$

It can now be shown that, for all projection operators P, (IV.27) and (IV.28) can be satisfied only by $M(P) = \mathrm{Tr}(PW)$

with positive definite Hermitian operators W with $\mathrm{Tr}\,W = 1$. An extension of the possible ensembles beyond those characterized by such W is therefore impossible under fairly general conditions. Consequently, we shall assume the general explanation of quantum mechanics given above with respect to the following correlation.

Every actually producible ensemble can be characterized by a suitable positive definite Hermitian operator W with $\mathrm{Tr}\,W = 1$, and every performable Yes–No measurement by a suitable projection operator P, with mutually orthogonal P_i representing exclusive but combinable Yes–No measurements and $P = \sum_i P_i$ representing in this case the measurement with the measured value 1 (= Yes) for "at least one of the P_i has the measured value 1".

Without being able to discuss the consequences of this interpretation for quantum mechanics in detail at this point, a consequence of the commutation relation (II.45) may be given briefly—the famous Heisenberg uncertainty relation.

The Schwartz inequality is necessary for its derivation. If φ and ψ are two vectors in the Hilbert space, it follows from $\varphi\|\psi^2\| = \psi(\psi, \varphi) + r$ by internal multiplication with ψ that $(\psi, r) = 0$. If we now take the square of the lengths on both sides of the equations, we obtain

$$\|\varphi\|^2 \, \|\psi\|^4 = \|\psi\|^2 \, |(\psi, \varphi)|^2 + \|r\|^2 .$$

For $\|\psi\| \neq 0$ we immediately obtain the Schwartz inequality:

$$\|\varphi\|^2 \, \|\psi\|^2 \geqq |(\psi, \varphi)|^2 , \tag{IV.29}$$

which is also satisfied trivially for $\psi = 0$. If the vectors φ and ψ are represented in particular by the sets of numbers $\{a_\nu\}$ and $\{b_\nu\}$, respectively, it follows that

$$\left(\sum_\nu |a_\nu|^2\right) \left(\sum_\mu |b_\mu|^2\right) \geqq \left| \sum_\nu a_\nu^* b_\nu \right|^2 . \tag{IV.30}$$

If, now, W is any ensemble, the mean values of momentum and position are given by $M(p) = \mathrm{Tr}(pW)$ and $M(q) = \mathrm{Tr}(qW)$.

If we put $\mathscr{P} = p - M(p)$ and $Q = q - M(q)$, the mean values $M(\mathscr{P}^2)$ and $M(Q^2)$ are the deviations of the measured values of the momentum (or the position) about the mean. Let us put

$$\Delta p^2 = M(\mathscr{P}^2), \qquad \Delta q^2 = M(Q^2).$$

Then

$$\Delta p^2 \Delta q^2 = \mathrm{Tr}(\mathscr{P}^2 W)\,\mathrm{Tr}(Q^2 W).$$

Since W can be written in the form $W = \sum_\nu w_\nu P_{\varphi_\nu}$ with the eigenvalues w_ν and eigenvectors φ_ν, with $0 \leqq w_\nu \leqq 1$ and also, because $\mathrm{Tr}\,W = 1$, $\sum_\nu w_\nu = 1$, it follows (easily when the c.o.s. of the φ_ν is selected specially to calculate the trace) that:

$$\mathrm{Tr}(\mathscr{P}^2 W) = \sum_\nu w_\nu(\varphi_\nu, \mathscr{P}^2 \varphi_\nu) = \sum_\nu w_\nu \|\mathscr{P}\varphi_\nu\|^2.$$

According to the Schwartz inequality in the form (IV.30), therefore,

$$\Delta p^2 \Delta q^2 = \sum_\nu w_\nu \|\mathscr{P}\varphi_\nu\|^2 \sum_\mu w_\mu \|Q\varphi_\mu\|^2 \geqq \Big\{\sum_\nu w_\nu \|\mathscr{P}\varphi_\nu\|\;\|Q\varphi_\mu\|\Big\}^2.$$

By means of the Schwartz inequality in the form (IV.29) we obtain

$$\begin{aligned}\|\mathscr{P}\varphi_\nu\|\;\|Q\varphi_\mu\| &\geqq |(\mathscr{P}\varphi_\nu, Q\varphi)_\mu| \\ &\geqq \frac{1}{2}|(\mathscr{P}\varphi_\nu, Q\varphi_\mu) - (Q\varphi_\mu, \mathscr{P}\varphi_\nu)| \\ &= \frac{1}{2}|(\varphi_\nu, (\mathscr{P}Q - Q\mathscr{P})\,\varphi_\nu)| = \frac{\hbar}{2}\end{aligned}$$

and therefore

$$\Delta p\, \Delta q \geqq \frac{\hbar}{2}\sum_\nu w_\nu = \frac{\hbar}{2}. \qquad \text{(IV.31)}$$

This uncertainty relation states that in any experimentally producible ensemble the product of the spread in position and momentum cannot go below a lower limit given by Planck's constant.

However, in the physical interpretation sketched here, which does indeed formulate the principle of this interpretation clearly, many questions still remain open:

1. What W is to be correlated with which ensembles?
2. Which projection operators P are to be correlated with which Yes–No measurements?

Points 1 and 2 include the questions as to whether all W and all P exist as patterns of real ensembles and real possible measurements, and, if not, what part of the W or P is characterized by the fact that it can be used as a mathematical picture of the real ensembles or measurements.

No definitive answer to the questions just raised is possible even today. Here we shall briefly take the standpoint, which was taken as a starting-point right at the beginning of quantum mechanics and from which we start even today when concrete problems of the quantum theory are to be treated. This starting-point is provided by the operators p_i for the momenta and q_i for the positions (in Cartesian coordinates). We either assume the commutation relations (III.2) or start directly from the coordinate representation (III.3). Consequently, the appropriate operators are determined for all questions of momentum and position values, since the spectral representations of these operations are also known. The next step is the attempt to deduce from quantities known from classical point mechanics (such as, for example the energy) the corresponding operators by replacing the classical p_i, q_i by the known operators. In this way we obtain a very far-reaching scheme of quantum theory by means of which (supplemented by a description of the spin of the particles) a large number of facts can be described.

Question (1) relating to the W is then reduced indirectly to question (2): if we know $\mathrm{Tr}(PW)$ for all P, W is thereby unambiguously determined since from $\mathrm{Tr}(P(W_1 - W_2)) = 0$ for all P it immediately follows that $W_1 = W_2$. However, it is by no means necessary to know $\mathrm{Tr}(PW)$ for all P. If, for example, $\mathrm{Tr}(P_\psi W) = 1$, it follows that $(\psi, W\psi) = 1$ and therefore

$(\psi, (1 - W)\psi) = 0$. Since $(1 - W)$ is positive definite, we must† have $(1 - W)\psi = 0$ and therefore $W\psi = \psi : \psi$ is therefore an eigenvector of W with the eigenvalue 1. Since the $\sum_{\nu} w_{\nu}$ for all eigenvalues of W is equal to 1, $W = P_{\psi}$. If therefore the measurement of P_{ψ} in the ensemble concerned is always positive, $W = P_{\psi}$. Other quantities can be measured for this ensemble $W = P_{\psi}$. However, it must be stressed that this must not be done, for example, on the objects used previously in the test, since these may possibly have been affected by the "measuring apparatus P_{ψ}". Rather is "the apparatus forming the ensemble $W = P_{\psi}$" to be tested by means of the "measuring apparatus P_{ψ}" with respect to just its property of yielding an ensemble of the form P_{ψ}.

The last remarks indicate that the two questions (1) and (2) include still other physical problems: namely in (1) that of the physical understanding of the preparation apparatus, i.e. those which produce the populations, and in (2) that of the physical understanding of the measuring apparatus and therefore of the whole of the measuring process. What we have touched on here in the form of questions is a systematic theory of preparing and measuring apparatus, which is naturally carried out in any particular concrete case by technical men and experimental physicists before the construction of such apparatus, e.g. for the construction of a large electron-synchrotron for the production of desired ensembles of electrons or for the construction of a bubble chamber for the measurement of particles.

But even when we disregard the problems (1) and (2) of the concrete arrangement there is another, more far-reaching, question open: namely, whether it is not possible from relatively general laws on preparation and measurement to deduce that the scheme of the Hilbert space with the W and P is precisely that which is suitable for Nature. This is the problem of an axiomatic foundation of quantum mechanics, at least in relation

† $(\psi, (1 - W)\psi) = (\psi, (\sqrt{1 - W})^2 \psi) = \|\sqrt{1 - W}\psi\|^2 = 0$
or: $\sqrt{1 - W}\,\psi = 0$ and therefore $\sqrt{1 - W}\sqrt{1 - W}\,\psi = (1 - W)\psi = 0$.

to its most general basic structure. The historical development of quantum mechanics did not take this path; on the contrary, individual relationships showed the structure of quantum mechanics inductively, as the original papers given in this book are in fact intended to demonstrate.

To sketch briefly what should be understood, for example, by an axiomatic foundation we may refer to the example of thermodynamics, where all the consequences are derived from the law of the impossibility of perpetual motion (first law = energy law) and the law on the impossibility of a so-called perpetual motion machine of the second kind (second law = entropy law), without its being possible to prove such extremely general laws directly by experiment—in fact, these have to be regarded as proved by their experimentally confirmed consequences. In spite of very interesting attempts, this axiomatic foundation has not yet been solved in an absolutely satisfactory manner for the basic structure of quantum mechanics (i.e. for Hilbert space, ensembles W, and Yes–No measurements P), since either it has not yet been possible to derive Hilbert space from the axioms used as a basis, or the axioms used as a basis are not completely understandable physically.

After this look at problems still partially unsolved, we shall turn to the question of temporal development within quantum mechanics.

CHAPTER V

Temporal Development of the Physical Quantities

FOR the temporal development, Heisenberg, Born and Jordan, on the one hand, and Schrödinger, on the other hand, give a certain procedure which we shall formulate in both cases in the symbolism of Hilbert space. According to Born and Jordan this formulation for the temporal change of the observables A runs

$$\frac{\hbar}{i}\dot{A} = HA - AH. \tag{V.1}$$

The formulation of the time-dependent Schrödinger equation runs

$$-\frac{\hbar}{i}\dot{\psi} = H\psi. \tag{V.2}$$

In his paper on the relationship of the Heisenberg–Born–Jordan quantum mechanics to wave mechanics, Schrödinger showed that the time-dependence of the matrix elements formed with the time-dependent vectors according to (V.2) were the same as in Heisenberg's case. With the aid of the formulae for interpreting quantum mechanics it is now easy to show the equivalence of (V.1) and (V.2).

Both equations (V.1) and (V.2) can easily be integrated formally. The operator

$$U(t) = e^{-(i/\hbar)Ht} \tag{V.3}$$

is unitary since $UU^* = U^*U = 1$.† From (V.3) we obtain

$$\dot{U} = -\frac{i}{\hbar} UH$$

and also from

$$U^* = e^{(i/\hbar)Ht}$$

we obtain

$$\dot{U}^* = \frac{i}{\hbar} HU^*.$$

The solution of (V.1) can therefore be written

$$A(t) = U^*(t)\, A(0)\, U(t) \tag{V.4}$$

and the solution of (V.2):

$$\psi(t) = U(t)\, \psi(0). \tag{V.5}$$

Formulae (V.1) or (V.4) are called the Heisenberg picture and (V.2) or (V.5) the Schrödinger picture of time-dependence. In the Heisenberg picture, the expectations value of the observable $A(t)$ can be calculated by means of an operator W for the ensemble which is constant in time:

$$M(A(t)) = \mathrm{Tr}(A(t)\, W) = \mathrm{Tr}\big(U^*(t)\, A(0)\, U(t)\, W\big). \tag{V.6}$$

In the Schrödinger picture, on the other hand, the operators assigned to the observables $\left(\text{e.g. } \frac{\hbar}{i}\frac{d}{dx} \text{ for the momentum}\right)$ are left constant in time and the vector ψ characterizing the ensemble changes in the ensemble with the time. For the observable A in the ensemble $\psi(t)$ we then have

$$M_t(A) = \mathrm{Tr}(AP_{\psi(t)}) = \big(\psi(t), A\psi(t)\big).$$

We shall generalize this formula for the case of any desired ensemble W. Since

$$P_{\psi(t)}\varphi = \psi(t)\, (\psi(t), \varphi) = U(t)\, \psi(0)\, \big(U(t)\, \psi(0), \varphi\big)$$
$$= U(t)\, \psi(0)\, (\psi(0), U^*(t)\, \varphi)$$

† U^* is the Hermitian conjugate operator of U defined by $(\varphi, U\psi) = (U^*\varphi, \psi)$.

we have $P_{\psi(t)} = U(t)\, P_{\psi(0)} U^*(t)$, which we generalize to

$$W(t) = U(t)\, W(0)\, U^*(t).$$

Consequently, then

$$M_t(A) = \mathrm{Tr}(AW(t)) = \mathrm{Tr}(AU(t)\, W(0)\, U^*(t)). \quad \text{(V.7)}$$

Since $\mathrm{Tr}(AB) = \mathrm{Tr}(BA)$,† it follows from (V.7) that

$$M_t(A) = \mathrm{Tr}(U^*(t)\, AU(t)\, W(0)).$$

Formulae (V.6) and (V.7) are therefore identical, i.e. give the same physical statements if we put

$$A = A(0) \quad \text{and} \quad W = W(0).$$

This summarizes all the foundations of quantum mechanics. Its further development consists in the application of these methods to the most diverse physical systems and questions. Many methods have been developed that are adapted for one problem or another. Even now, new fields of quantum mechanics are continually being made accessible methodically such as, for example, systems of very many interacting particles such as are present in macroscopic objects. Thus, there are three directions in which quantum mechanics must still be supplemented and extended today (quite apart from quantum field theory and elementary particle physics):

1. The development of mathematical methods capable of handling even relatively complicated systems.
2. The theory of the preparation of ensembles and of measurement, i.e. the problem of assigning the populations to certain positive definite Hermitian operators with a trace equal to 1 and the measurements to certain Hermitian operators.

† $\mathrm{Tr}(AB) = \sum_{\nu\mu} a_{\nu\mu} b_{\mu\nu} = \sum_{\nu\mu} b_{\mu\nu} a_{\nu\mu} = \mathrm{Tr}(BA)$ with $a_{\nu\mu} = (\psi_\nu, A\psi_\mu)$ and $b_{\nu\mu} = (\varphi_\nu, B\varphi_\mu)$, in which the φ_ν form a c.o.s.

3. The axiomatic foundation of quantum mechanics, i.e. the derivation of the Hilbert space structure as a transformation of fundamental structures in the physics of measurement and preparation.

PART 2

PAPER 1

Investigations on Quantum Theory†‡

LOUIS DE BROGLIE

Introduction

THE history of optical theories shows that the scientific view has for long oscillated between a mechanical and an undulatory conception of light; however, these two views are perhaps less opposed to one another than was previously thought, and the development of quantum theory, in particular, appears to confirm the latter idea.

On the basis of the idea of a generally valid relationship between the concepts of frequency and energy, we start in this paper from the existence of a certain periodic process of an as yet not more closely specified nature which must be assigned to each isolated portion of energy and which depends on its eigenmass in accordance with the Planck–Einstein relation. Then the relativity theory requires the assignment to the uniform movement of each material point of the propagation of a certain wave the phase of which propagates in space with a velocity greater than that of light (Chapter 1).

† *Annales de Physique*, **3**, 22, 1925. (This is the text of de Broglie's 1924 Doctoral Thesis.)

‡ Parts of this and other papers which are omitted are indicated by a row of dots; see, for instance, p. 75.

Chapter 1. The Phase Wave

1. The Quantum Relation and the Theory of Relativity

One of the most important new concepts which the theory of relativity has introduced is the inertia of energy. According to Einstein, mass must be assigned to any energy and any mass represents energy. Mass and energy are always connected with one another by the general relation:

$$\text{energy} = \text{mass} \times c^2,$$

where c is a constant, the so-called "velocity of light" which we, however, prefer for reasons to be given later to call the "limiting velocity of energy". Since, therefore, there is always proportionality between mass and energy, mass and energy must be regarded as two equally valid expressions denoting the same physical reality.

The atomic theory and, later, the electron theory have taught us that we must regard matter as essentially discontinuous, and this leads us to the assumption that, in contrast to older ideas on the nature of light, all forms of energy are completely concentrated in small regions of space or, at least, are concentrated about certain singular points.

The principle of the inertia of energy assigns to every body the eigenmass of which (i.e. the mass measured by the observer in the same system) is m_0 an eigenenergy m_0c^2. If the body is in uniform motion with velocity $v = \beta \cdot c$ relative to the observer, whom we shall assume at rest, its mass will have for the observer the value

$$\frac{m_0}{\sqrt{1-\beta^2}}$$

according to a well-known formula of relativistic dynamics, and its energy is therefore

$$\frac{m_0c^2}{\sqrt{1-\beta^2}}.$$

Since the kinetic energy can be regarded as the increase in the energy of the body for the observer at rest when the body passes from the state of rest to the state of motion with velocity $v = \beta \cdot c$, we find the following expression for its value:

$$E_{\text{kin}} = \frac{m_0c^2}{\sqrt{1-\beta^2}} - m_0c^2 = m_0c^2\left(\frac{1}{\sqrt{1-\beta^2}} - 1\right),$$

which naturally passes into the classical value for small values of β:

$$E_{\text{kin}} = \tfrac{1}{2}mv^2.$$

Now that we have recalled this, we shall turn to the question in what form we can introduce quanta into relativistic dynamics. The basic idea of quantum theory is, of course, the impossibility of considering an isolated fragment of energy without assigning a certain frequency to it. This coupling of concepts is expressed in the following relation, which I will call the quantum relation:

$$\text{energy} = h \cdot \text{frequency},$$

where h is Planck's constant.

. . . . .

It can therefore be assumed that because of a general law of nature a periodic phenomenon of frequency ν_0 is associated with each fragment of energy with eigenmass m_0 by the relation:

$$h\nu_0 = m_0c^2.$$

Here, ν_0 is, as must be particularly noted, measured in the system fixed to the fragment of energy. This hypothesis is the basis of our theory: it applies, like all hypotheses, to the same extent as the conclusions that can be drawn from it.

. . . . .

After we have assumed the existence of a frequency to be assigned to the fragment of energy, we turn to the question of in what way this frequency makes itself manifest to the above-mentioned fixed observer. The Lorentz–Einstein time transformation teaches us that a periodic event associated with the moving body slows down for the fixed observer in the ratio of 1 to $\sqrt{1-\beta^2}$; this is the well-known phenomenon of the slowing-down of clocks. Consequently, the frequency measured by the fixed observer is

$$\nu_1 = \nu_0 \sqrt{1-\beta^2} = \frac{m_0 c^2}{h} \sqrt{1-\beta^2}\,.$$

On the other hand, however, since the energy of the moving particle for the fixed observer is

$$\frac{m_0 c^2}{\sqrt{1-\beta^2}}$$

the corresponding frequency according to the quantum relation is

$$\nu = \frac{1}{h} \frac{m_0 c^2}{\sqrt{1-\beta^2}}\,.$$

These two frequencies ν_1 and ν are basically different, since they contain the factor $\sqrt{1-\beta^2}$ in different forms. Here there is a difficulty which has occupied me for a long time; I succeeded in eliminating it by proving the following theorem, which I will call the theorem of phase agreement:

"The periodic phenomenon fixed to the moving particle, which has the frequency $\nu_1 = \frac{1}{h} m_0 c^2 \sqrt{1-\beta^2}$ with respect to the observer at rest appears to this observer always in phase with a wave of the frequency $\nu = \frac{1}{h} m_0 c^2 \frac{1}{\sqrt{1-\beta^2}}$ propagating in the direction of motion of the moving particle with the velocity $V = \frac{c}{\beta}$."

The proof is very simple. It is assumed that at time $t = 0$ there is phase agreement between the periodic phenomenon associated with the moving particle and the wave defined above.

At time t, the moving particle has travelled a distance $x = \beta ct$ and the phase of the periodic phenomenon has changed by

$$\nu_1 t = \frac{m_0 c^2}{h} \sqrt{1-\beta^2} \cdot \frac{x}{\beta c}.$$

The phase of the part of the wave that covers the moving particle has changed by

$$\nu\left(t - \frac{\beta x}{c}\right) = \frac{m_0 c^2}{h} \frac{1}{\sqrt{1-\beta^2}} \left(\frac{x}{\beta c} - \frac{\beta x}{c}\right)$$

$$= \frac{m_0 c^2}{h} \sqrt{1-\beta^2} \cdot \frac{x}{\beta c}.$$

Thus, phase agreement exists as we have stated.

Another proof can be given for this theorem which is in fact basically identical with that just given but has perhaps a still more surprising effect. If t_0 represents the time of an observer associated with the moving particle (eigentime of the moving particle), the Lorentz transformation gives:

$$t_0 = \frac{1}{\sqrt{1-\beta^2}} \left(t - \frac{\beta x}{c}\right).$$

The periodic phenomenon considered by us is represented for the same observer by a sine function of $\nu_0 t_0$. For the fixed observer it is represented by the same sine function of

$$\nu_0 \frac{1}{\sqrt{1-\beta^2}} \left(t - \frac{\beta x}{c}\right)$$

that characterises a wave of the frequency $\frac{\nu_0}{\sqrt{1-\beta^2}}$ propagating with the velocity $\frac{c}{\beta}$ in the same direction as the moving particle.

It is unavoidably necessary to return to the nature of the wave the existence of which has just been assumed. The fact that its velocity $V = \frac{c}{\beta}$ is necessarily greater than c (β is always smaller than 1, since otherwise the mass would become infinite or imaginary) shows that in no case can it be an energy-transferring wave. On the contrary, our theory shows that it represents the distribution of the phases of an event in space; it is therefore a "phase wave".

. . . . .

2. Phase Velocity and Group Velocity

We shall now derive an important relation existing between the velocity of the moving particle and that of the phase wave. If waves of closely adjacent frequencies propagate in the same direction Ox with the velocity V, which we shall call the velocity of phase propagation, these waves will give beat phenomena by superposition if the velocity V changes with the frequency ν. These phenomena have been investigated, in particular, by Lord Rayleigh for the case of dispersive media.

We therefore consider two waves with adjacent frequencies ν and $\nu + \delta\nu$ and velocities V and $V' = V + \frac{dV}{d\nu}\delta\nu$; their superposition is represented analytically by the following equation, which is obtained by neglecting terms of the second order in $\delta\nu$ as compared with ν:

$$\sin 2\pi\left(\nu t - \frac{\nu x}{V} + \varphi\right) + \sin 2\pi\left(\nu' t - \frac{\nu' x}{V'} + \varphi'\right)$$

$$= 2 \sin 2\pi\left(\nu t - \frac{\nu x}{V} + \psi\right)$$

$$\times \cos 2\pi\left[\frac{\delta\nu}{2} t - x\frac{d\left(\frac{\nu}{V}\right)}{d\nu}\cdot\frac{\delta\nu}{2} + \psi'\right].$$

Again, therefore, we obtain a sine wave, the amplitude of which is changed by the frequency $\delta\nu$ since the sign of the cosine makes little difference. This is a well-known result. If we denote by U the velocity of propagation of the beats or the group velocity of the waves, we find

$$\frac{1}{U} = \frac{d\left(\frac{\nu}{V}\right)}{d\nu}.$$

Let us return to a consideration of the phase waves. Let us assign to the moving particle a velocity $v = \beta c$, not giving β a completely determined value but only assuming that this value is between β and $\beta + \delta\beta$; the frequencies of the corresponding phase waves are then in the small interval ν, $\nu + \delta\nu$.

We now state the following law, which will be useful to us later. "The group velocity of the phase waves is equal to the velocity of the moving particle." In fact, the group velocity is actually determined by the formula given above in which V and ν can be regarded as functions of β according to the relations:

$$V = \frac{c}{\beta}, \qquad \nu = \frac{1}{h}\frac{m_0c^2}{\sqrt{1-\beta^2}}.$$

We can write:

$$U = \frac{\frac{d\nu}{\beta}}{\frac{d\left(\frac{\nu}{V}\right)}{d\beta}};$$

but now

$$\frac{d\nu}{d\beta} = \frac{m_0c^2}{h}\frac{\beta}{(1-\beta^2)^{3/2}}$$

$$\frac{d\left(\frac{\nu}{V}\right)}{d\beta} = \frac{m_0c^2}{h}\frac{d\left(\frac{\beta}{\sqrt{1-\beta^2}}\right)}{d\beta} = \frac{m_0c^2}{h}\frac{1}{(1-\beta^2)^{3/2}},$$

so that:

$$U = \beta \cdot c = v.$$

The group velocity of the phase waves therefore coincides with the velocity of the moving particle. This result requires an observation: in the wave theory of dispersion, apart from the absorption regions, the velocity of the energy is equal to the group velocity. Here we find a similar result from a quite different point of view, since the velocity of the moving particle is nothing other than the velocity of displacement of energy.

. . . . .

Chapter 2. The Maupertuis and the Fermat Principles

1. Contents of this Chapter

In this chapter we shall undertake an attempt to generalise the results of Chapter 1 for the case of a particle not moving uniformly in a straight line. This modified motion assumes the presence of some field of force acting on the moving particle. For us, a field of force will be an electromagnetic field, and the mechanics of the modified motion then consists in the study of the motion of an electrically charged body in an electromagnetic field.

. . . . .

The phase wave accompanying the motion of a particle has, if our ideas are adopted, properties which depend on the nature of the moving particle since, for example, its frequency is determined by the total energy. Consequently, the condition appears to be satisfied that in the action of a field of force on the moving particle this field also exerts an influence on the propagation of the phase wave. Guided by the idea of a close relationship between the principle of least action and the Fermat principle, from the very beginning of my investigations on this subject I was led to the *assumption* that for a given value of the total energy of the moving particle and therefore of the frequency of its phase wave the mechanically possible paths of the particle coincide with the possible rays of the phase wave.

. . . . .

2. The Two Principles of Least Action in Classical Dynamics

The principle of least action in classical mechanics can be stated in the Hamiltonian form as follows:

> "The equations of dynamics can be derived from the requirement that the integral
>
> $$\int_{t_1}^{t_2} L\, dt,$$
>
> taken between fixed time limits for given initial and final values of the parameters q_i that determine the state of the system shall have a stationary value."

According to definition, L is called the Lagrangian and depends only on the variables q_i and $\dot{q}_i = \frac{dq_i}{dt}$. We therefore have

$$\delta \int_{t_1}^{t_2} L\, dt = 0.$$

From this the so-called Lagrangian equations are obtained by a method known from the calculus of variations:

$$\frac{d}{dt}\left(\frac{\partial L}{\partial \dot{q}_i}\right) = \frac{\partial L}{\partial q_i},$$

their number being equal to the number of variables q_i.

It still remains to define the function L. Classical mechanics puts

$$L = E_{\text{kin}} - E_{\text{pot}},$$

the difference between the kinetic and potential energies. We shall see below that relativistic dynamics uses a value different from L.

Let us now go over to the principle of least action in Maupertuis' form. In this connection, we may first mention that the Lagrangian equations in the above general form possess a first integral, the so-called "energy of the system", which is equal to

$$W = -L + \sum_i \frac{\partial L}{\partial \dot{q}_i} \dot{q}_i,$$

again assuming that the function L does not depend explicitly on the time, as we always assume in what follows. Then we have in fact:

$$\frac{dW}{dt} = -\sum_i \frac{\partial L}{\partial q_i} \dot{q}_i - \sum_i \frac{\partial L}{\partial \dot{q}_i} \ddot{q}_i + \sum_i \frac{\partial L}{\partial \dot{q}_i} \ddot{q}_i + \sum_i \frac{d}{dt}\left(\frac{\partial L}{\partial \dot{q}_i}\right) \dot{q}_i$$

$$= \sum_i \dot{q}_i \left[\frac{d}{dt}\left(\frac{\partial L}{\partial \dot{q}_i}\right) - \frac{\partial L}{\partial q_i}\right],$$

a quantity which vanishes according to the Lagrangian equations. Consequently if follows that:

$$W = \text{const.}$$

We now apply the Hamiltonian principle to all "varied" paths that lead from a given starting point A to a given end-point B and correspond to a given value of the energy W. Since W, t_1, and t_2 are constants, we may write:

$$\delta \int_{t}^{t_2} L\,dt = \delta \int_{t_1}^{t_2} (L + W)\,dt = 0,$$

or alternatively:

$$\delta \int_{t_1}^{t_2} \sum_i \frac{\partial L}{\partial \dot{q}_i} \dot{q}_i\,dt = \delta \int_{A}^{B} \sum_i \frac{\partial L}{\partial \dot{q}_i}\,dq_i = 0,$$

the last integral extending over all values of the q_i between A and B in such a way that the time is eliminated; it is no longer permissible in the form now obtained to prescribe any restriction for the time limit. On the contrary, all changed paths must correspond to one and the same value of the energy W.†

We now give the classical formulation of the canonical equations:

$$p_i = \frac{\partial L}{\partial \dot{q}_i}.$$

The momenta are the conjugate momenta of the variables q_i. The Maupertuis principle can be written in terms of classical mechanics as:

$$\delta \int_A^B \sum_i p_i \, dq_i = 0,$$

in which $L = E_{\text{kin}} - E_{\text{pot}}$, E_{pot} is independent of the $\dot{q}_i$, and E_{kin} is a homogeneous quadratic function. As a consequence of Euler's theorem, we then have

$$\sum_i p_i \, dq_i = \sum_i p_i \dot{q}_i \, dt = 2E_{\text{kin}} \, dt.$$

For a material point, $E_{\text{kin}} = \frac{1}{2} mv^2$, and the principle of least action assumes its earliest-known form:

$$\delta \int_A^B mv \, dl = 0,$$

where dl is an element of the path.

3. The Two Principles of Least Action in the Dynamics of the Electron

We now turn again to the question of the dynamics of the electron from a relativistic standpoint. Here we must understand the term "electron" in the general sense of a material point bearing an electric charge. We shall assume that the electron outside any field has a rest mass m_0; its electric charge is denoted by e.

† In order to make the proof rigid, it is necessary to permit the limits t_1 and t_2 to vary in a well-known manner; but, because of the time-independence of the result, our procedure is not wrong.

We shall again consider the space-time system; let the space coordinates be x^1, x^2, x^3 and the coordinate ct be x^4. The fundamental invariant, the "length element" is defined by the equation

$$ds = \sqrt{(dx^4)^2 - (dx^1)^2 - (dx^2)^2 - (dx^3)^2}\,.$$

In this section, as in the following ones, we shall always use the notation of tensor calculus.

At each point a world line possesses a tangent the direction of which is determined by the "world velocity vector" of unit length, the contravariant components of which are given by the equation:

$$u^i = \frac{dx^i}{ds} \qquad (i = 1, 2, 3, 4).$$

The relation $u^i \cdot u_i = 1$ is immediately verified.

A moving particle may describe the world line; let it possess a velocity $v = \beta c$ with components v_x, v_y, v_z when it passes through the point under consideration. The components of the world velocity vector are:

$$u_1 = -u^1 = -\frac{v_x}{c\sqrt{1-\beta^2}}, \qquad u_2 = -u^2 = -\frac{v_y}{c\sqrt{1-\beta^2}};$$

$$u_3 = -u^3 = -\frac{v_x}{c\sqrt{1-\beta^2}}; \qquad u_4 = u^4 = \frac{1}{\sqrt{1-\beta^2}}.$$

For the purpose of the definition of an electromagnetic field, we must introduce a second world vector the components of which are represented as a function of the vector potential a and the scalar potential ψ by the equations:

$$\varphi_1 = -\varphi^1 = -a_x; \qquad \varphi_2 = -\varphi^2 = -a_y;$$

$$\varphi_3 = -\varphi^3 = -a_z; \qquad \varphi_4 = +\varphi^4 = \frac{1}{c}\psi.$$

Let us now consider two points P and Q in the space-time system that correspond to the given values of the space and time coordinates. We can examine a line integral that is taken along the world line from P to Q; naturally, the function to be integrated must be invariant.

Let

$$\int_P^Q (-m_0 c - e\varphi_i u^i)\, ds = \int_P^Q (-m_0 c u_i - e\varphi^i)\, u^i\, ds$$

be this integral. The Hamiltonian principle states that, if the world line of a moving particle passes through P and Q, it has such a form that the above-defined integral has a stationary value.

We define a third world vector by the relation:

$$J_i = m_0 c u_i + e\varphi_i \qquad (i = 1, 2, 3, 4);$$

then the law of least action assumes the form:

$$\delta \int_P^Q (J_1\, dx^1 + J_2\, dx^2 + J_3\, dx^3 + J_4\, dx^4) = \delta \int_P^Q J_i\, dx^i = 0.$$

Below we shall assign a physical meaning to the world vector J.

Now we return to the usual form of the dynamic equations by replacing ds in the first form of the action integral by $c\, dt \sqrt{1 - \beta^2}$. From this it follows that:

$$\delta \int_{t_1}^{t_2} [-m_0 c^2 \sqrt{1 - \beta^2} - ec\varphi_4 - e(\varphi_1 v_x + \varphi_2 v_y + \varphi_3 v_z)]\, dt = 0,$$

in which t_1 and t_2 correspond to the points P and Q of the space-time system.

When a purely electrostatic field is present, the quantities $\varphi_1, \varphi_2, \varphi_3$ are equal to zero and the Lagrangian assumes the form:

$$L = -m_0 c^2 \sqrt{1 - \beta^2} - e\psi$$

which is often useful.

In all cases, since the Hamiltonian principle invariably has the form

$$\delta \int_{t_1}^{t_2} L\, dt = 0$$

we are always led to the Lagrangian equations

$$\frac{d}{dt}\left(\frac{\partial L}{\partial \dot{q}_i}\right) = \frac{\partial L}{\partial q_i} \qquad (i = 1, 2, 3).$$

When the potentials do not depend on the time, we always obtain the energy law again

$$W = -L + \sum_i p_i q_i = \text{const.}, \quad p_i = \frac{\partial L}{\partial \dot{q}_i} \quad (i = 1, 2, 3.)$$

If the argument given earlier above is followed exactly, we obtain the Maupertuis principle:

$$\delta \int_A^B \sum p_i \, dq_i = 0,$$

if A and B are two space points that correspond for the reference system used to the points P and Q of the space-time system.

The quantities p_1, p_2, p_3, which are equal to the partial derivatives of the function L with respect to the corresponding velocities, can be used for the definition of the vector $\boldsymbol{p}$, which we shall call "momentum vector". If no magnetic field is present, the components of this vector are:

$$p_x = \frac{m_0 v_x}{\sqrt{1-\beta^2}}, \quad p_y = \frac{m_0 v_y}{\sqrt{1-\beta^2}}, \quad p_z = \frac{m_0 v_z}{\sqrt{1-\beta^2}}.$$

It is therefore identical with the linear momentum, and the Maupertuis action integral has the simple form used by Maupertuis himself with the sole difference that the mass depends on the velocity in accordance with Lorentz's law.

If a magnetic field is present, the following expressions are found for the components of the momentum vector:

$$p_x = \frac{m_0 c_x}{\sqrt{1-\beta^2}} + e a_x, \quad p_y = \frac{m_0 v_y}{\sqrt{1-\beta^2}} + e a_y,$$

$$p_z = \frac{m_0 v_z}{\sqrt{1-\beta^2}} + e a_z.$$

Now there is no longer identity between the vector $\boldsymbol{p}$ and the linear momentum; consequently, the expression for the action integral is more complicated.

Let us consider a moving particle of given total energy present in a field; at any point of the field that the moving particle can reach its velocity is determined by the energy equation, but the direction may be *a priori* undetermined. The expressions for p_x, p_y, and p_z show that the momentum vector at each point of an electrostatic field has the same magnitude whatever the direction concerned may be. This no longer applies when there is a magnetic field: the magnitude of the vector $\boldsymbol{p}$ then depends on the angle between the direction concerned and the vector potential, as can be seen by calculating the expression

$$p_x^2 + p_y^2 + p_z^2.$$

This observation will be of use later.

At the end of this section we look into the physical significance of the world vector J on which the Hamiltonian integral depends. We have defined it by the equation:

$$J_i = m_0cu_i + e\varphi_i \qquad (i = 1, 2, 3, 4).$$

Because of the values of u_i and φ_i it follows that

$$J_i = -p_x, \qquad J_2 = -p_y, \qquad J_3 = -p_z, \qquad J_4 = \frac{W}{c}.$$

The contravariant components are:

$$J^1 = p_x, \qquad J^2 = p_y. \qquad J^3 = p_z, \qquad J^4 = \frac{W}{c}.$$

We are therefore dealing with the well-known "energy-momentum vector" which includes the energy and the momentum.

From the equation

$$\delta \int_P^Q J_i dx^i = 0 \quad (i = 1, 2, 3, 4)$$

it immediately follows, if J_4 is constant, that:

$$\delta \int_A^B J_i \, dx^i = 0 \quad (i = 1, 2, 3).$$

This is the shortest form in which the principle of action can be stated.

4. Propagation of the Waves; Fermat's Principle

We now turn to the question of the propagation of the phase of a sine wave, which we shall investigate by a method analogous to that which we have used in the last two sections. Consequently, we first take a very general standpoint, and again we shall investigate the space–time system.

Let us investigate the function $\sin \varphi$, in which the differential of φ is assumed to be dependent on the space and time variables x^i. In the space–time system there exists an infinite multiplicity of world lines along which the function φ is constant.

The wave theory in the form known through the work of Huyghens and Fresnel teaches us to select certain of these lines the projections of which on the space of the observer are for him the "rays" in the usual optical sense.

Let, as above, P and Q be two points of the space–time system. What is the form of the ray-determining law when the ray passes through the two points?

We consider the line integral $\int_Q^P d\varphi$ and take the Hamiltonian principle as that determining the ray:

$$\delta \int_P^Q d\varphi = 0.$$

The integral must in fact be stationary, since otherwise disturbances which at a certain point of space leave phase agreement intact and which cross again after they have traversed somewhat different paths would lead to different phases at that point.

The phase φ is an invariant; however, when we put:

$$d\varphi = 2\pi(O_1\,dx^1 + O_2\,dx^2 + O_3\,dx^3 + O_4\,dx^4) = 2\pi O_i\,dx^i,$$

the quantities O_i which are in general functions of x^i become the covariant components of a world vector, the world wave vector. If l is the direction of the ray in the usual sense, in the customary way $d\varphi$ is given in the form:

$$d\varphi = 2\pi\left(r\,dt - \frac{\nu}{V}\,dl\right),$$

where ν is the frequency and V the velocity of propagation. Then, we can also put:

$$O_1 = -\frac{\nu}{V}\cos(x, l) \qquad O_2 = -\frac{\nu}{V}\cos(y, l)$$

$$O_3 = -\frac{\nu}{V}\cos(z, l) \qquad O_4 = \frac{\nu}{c}.$$

The wave vector is therefore composed of the time component proportional to the frequency and a space vector $\boldsymbol{n}$ of magnitude $\frac{\nu}{V}$ and the direction of the wave propagation. We shall call this vector "wave number", since it is equal to the reciprocal of the wave length. If the frequency ν is constant, we pass from the Hamiltonian form

$$\delta\int_P^Q O_i\,dx^i = 0$$

to the Maupertuis equation:

$$\delta\int_A^B [O_1\,dx^1 + O_2\,dx^2 + O_3\,dx^3] = 0,$$

where A and B are the space points corresponding to P and Q.

If the values of O_1, O_2, and O_3 are inserted, it follows that

$$\delta\int_A^B \frac{\nu\,dl}{V} = 0.$$

In this form, Maupertuis' principle passes into the Fermat law.

Just as in the preceding sections a knowledge of the distribution of the $\boldsymbol{p}$ vector in the field was sufficient to find the path described by a particle of given total energy passing through two given points, here to determine the ray of a wave of given frequency passing through two given points only a knowledge of the spatial distribution of the wave number vector, through which the velocity of propagation is determined for each point in each direction, is necessary.

5. Extension of the Quantum Relation

We have now reached the most important point of the developments of this chapter. At the beginning we posed the question: "How does a phase wave assigned to a moving particle propagate when this particle moves non-uniformly in a field of force?" Instead of making tentative attempts, as I did at first, to determine the rate of propagation for each point in each direction, I shall undertake an extension of the quantum relationship which, it is true, is somewhat hypothetical, but which stands undoubtedly in close relation to relativistic ideas.

If w is the total energy of the moving particle and ν is the frequency of the corresponding phase wave, the relation $h\nu = w$ is satisfied. However, the last sections have shown us in what way two world vectors J and O can be defined that play completely analogous roles with respect to the study of a moving particle, on the one hand, and the propagation of a wave, on the other hand.

If we introduce these vectors, the relation $h\nu = w$ is written in the form:

$$O_4 = \frac{1}{h} J_4.$$

The fact that two vectors have a common component does not mean that the others are also the same. However, by means of a very obvious generalization we assume this to be the case and put:

$$O_i = \frac{1}{h} J_i \quad (i = 1, 2, 3, 4).$$

The change $d\varphi$ with respect to an element of the phase wave has the value

$$d\varphi = 2\pi O_i \, dx^i = \frac{2\pi}{h} J_i \, dx^i .$$

Fermat's principle then becomes:

$$\delta \int_A^B \sum_1^3 {}_i J_i \, dx^i = \delta \int_A^B \sum_1^3 {}_i p_i \, dx^i = 0.$$

Thus, we come to the statement of the following law:

"The application of Fermat's principle to the phase wave is identical with the application of Maupertuis' principle to the moving particle; the mechanically possible paths of the moving particle agree with the possible rays of the wave."

It can, indeed, be hoped that this idea of a deep-lying internal relationship between the two basic principles of geometrical optics and dynamics will become a reliable guide to the attempt to fuse the wave theory and the quantum theory.

The hypothesis of the proportionality of the vectors J and O is a kind of extension of the quantum relation the present form of which is very unsatisfactory, since it includes the energy but not the momentum inseparably associated with this. The new form is much more satisfactory, since it is represented by the equality of two world vectors.

. . . . .

Chapter 3. The Quantum-Theoretical Stability Conditions of Paths

1. The Bohr–Sommerfeld Stability Conditions

In 1917, Einstein gave the quantum condition a form invariant with respect to changes in coordinates.† We shall formulate this quantum condition for the case of closed paths;

† *Ber. d. Deutsch. Phys. Ges.*, 1917, p. 82.

it then has the following form:

$$\oint \sum_{1}^{3} {}_i p_i \, dq_i = nh \quad (n \text{ integral}),$$

in which the integral must extend over the whole of the path. In this form we again recognize Maupertuis' integral of action, which in fact plays an outstanding part in the quantum theory.

. . . . .

2. The Interpretation of the Einstein Condition

The concept of the phase wave permits us to clarify the Einstein condition. This clarification arises from the considerations of Chapter 2, according to which the path of the moving particle is one of the rays of its phase wave which propagates along the path with a constant frequency (since the total energy is constant) and changing velocity, the value of which we can calculate. The propagation is therefore analogous to that of a liquid wave in a closed channel of changing depth. It is physically evident that in order to have a stable state the length of the channel must be in resonance with the wave; in other words: the parts of the wave that follow one another at a distance that is an integral multiple of the length of the channel l and which therefore are located at the same point must be in phase with one another. The resonance condition is $l = n\lambda$ if the wave length is constant and $\oint \frac{\nu}{V} dl = n$ (integer) in the general case.

The integral appearing here is the same as in Fermat's principle; but we have now shown that this integral is equal to the Maupertuis action integral divided by h. The resonance condition is therefore identical with the quantum-theoretical stability condition.

This beautiful result, the derivation of which is so clear, provided that the basic ideas of the preceding chapters have been accepted, is the best justification of our type of treatment of the quantum problem.

In the special case of the circular orbits in the Bohr atom, we obtain $m_0 \oint v\,dl = 2\pi R m_0 v = nh$, or, since $v = \omega R$, if ω is the angular velocity:

$$m_0 \omega R^2 = n \frac{h}{2\pi}.$$

But this is, again, the simple Bohr stability condition.

PAPER 2

Quantization as an Eigenvalue Problem†

E. SCHRÖDINGER

(First Communication)

§ **1.** In this communication I should first like to show on the basis of the simplest case of the (non-relativistic and unperturbed) hydrogen atom that the usual quantization procedure can be replaced by another condition in which there is no longer any mention of "integers". On the contrary, the occurrence of integers follows in the same natural way as, for instance, in the case of the *number of nodes* of a vibrating string. The new form is capable of generalization and is very closely connected, I believe, with the true essence of the quantum laws.

The usual form of the latter is connected with the Hamiltonian partial differential equation:

$$H\left(q, \frac{\partial S}{\partial q}\right) = E. \tag{1}$$

A solution is sought to this equation which is a *sum* of functions each of a single one of the independent variables q.

We now introduce for S a new unknown ψ which is such that ψ will appear as a *product* of functions of the individual coordinates, i.e., we put

$$S = K \ln \psi. \tag{2}$$

The constant K must be introduced for dimensional reasons; it

† *Annalen der Physik*, **79**, 361, 1926.

has the dimensions of an *action*. Consequently, we obtain

$$H\left(q, \frac{K}{\psi}\frac{\partial \psi}{\partial q}\right) = E. \tag{1'}$$

We do *not* now seek a solution of the Equation (1′) but we set the following requirement. When the variability of mass is neglected always, and, when this is taken into account, at least when it relates to the *one*-electron problem, Equation (1′) can be brought into the form: quadratic form of ψ and its first derivatives $= 0$. We seek such functions ψ, real over the whole configuration space, unique-valued, finite, continuous and twice-differentiable, which make the integral of the quadratic form just mentioned† extended over the whole configuration space an *extremum*. *We replace the quantum conditions by this variational problem.*

We shall first assume for H the Hamiltonian function of the Kepler motion and show that the requirements set can be satisfied for *all positive* but only for a *discrete family of negative* values of E; i.e. the variational problem mentioned has a discrete and a continuous eigenvalue spectrum. The discrete spectrum corresponds to the Balmer terms and the continuous one to the energies of the hyperbolic paths. For numerical agreement to exist, K must have the value $h/2\pi$.

Since the choice of coordinates is immaterial for formulating the variational equations, we choose rectangular Cartesian coordinates. Then (1′) in our case (with e and m representing the charge and mass of the electron) runs:

$$\left(\frac{\partial \psi}{\partial x}\right)^2 + \left(\frac{\partial \psi}{\partial y}\right)^2 + \left(\frac{\partial \psi}{\partial z}\right)^2 - \frac{2m}{K^2}\left(E + \frac{e^2}{r}\right)\psi^2 = 0. \tag{1''}$$

$$r = \sqrt{x^2 + y^2 + z^2}\,.$$

And our variational problem is

$$\delta J = \delta \iiint dx\, dy\, dz \times \left[\left(\frac{\partial \psi}{\partial x}\right)^2 + \left(\frac{\partial \psi}{\partial y}\right)^2 + \left(\frac{\partial \psi}{\partial z}\right)^2 - \frac{2m}{K^2}\left(E + \frac{e^2}{r}\right)\psi^2\right] = 0, \tag{3}$$

† I realize that this formulation is not quite unambiguous.

the integral extending over the whole of space. From this we find in the usual manner

$$\frac{1}{2}\delta J = \int df\, \delta\psi \frac{\partial \psi}{\partial n} - \iiint dx\, dy\, dz\, \delta\psi$$

$$\times \left[\nabla^2\psi + \frac{2m}{K^2}\left(E + \frac{e^2}{r}\right)\psi\right] = 0. \tag{4}$$

Consequently, in the first place

$$\nabla^2\psi + \frac{2m}{K^2}\left(E + \frac{e^2}{r}\right)\psi = 0 \tag{5}$$

and in the second place the integral to extend over the infinitely distant closed surface must be

$$\int df\, \delta\psi \frac{\partial \psi}{\partial n} = 0. \tag{6}$$

(It will turn out that because of this last requirement we have to supplement our variational problem by a requirement concerning the behaviour of $\delta\psi$ at infinity, so that the above-mentioned *continuous* eigenvalue spectrum may also actually exist. This will be dealt with later.)

The solution of (5) can (*for example*) be effected in spherical polar coordinates r, ϑ, φ, by putting ψ as a product of one function each of r, ϑ, and φ. The method is sufficiently well known. We then obtain for the dependence on the polar angles a *spherical harmonic* and for the dependence on r—we shall call the function χ—we easily obtain the differential equation:

$$\frac{d^2\chi}{dr^2} + \frac{2}{r}\frac{d\chi}{dr} + \left(\frac{2mE}{K^2} + \frac{2me^2}{K^2 r} - \frac{n(n+1)}{r^2}\right)\chi = 0;$$

$$n = 0, 1, 2, 3\ldots \tag{7}$$

The limitation of n to integers is, as is well known, *necessary* for the dependence on the polar angles to be *unambiguous*. We require solutions of (7) that remain finite for all non-negative real values of r. Now,† the equation (7) in the complex r plane has *two* singularities at $r = 0$ and $r = \infty$, the second of which is a "position of uncertainty" (essentially singularity) of *all* the solutions, but the first is not (for no solution). These two singularities in fact form the *boundary points of our real interval.* In such cases, now, it is known that the requirement of *remaining* finite is equivalent to a *boundary condition* at the boundary points of the function χ. The equation has no solution at all *in general* that remains finite at *both* boundary points, such a solution existing only for certain particular values of the constants appearing in the equation. These particular values must be determined.

The subject matter just mentioned is the *central point* for the whole investigation.

We first consider the singular point $r = 0$. The so-called *determining fundamental equation* which determines the behaviour of the solutions at this point is

$$\varrho(\varrho - 1) + 2\varrho - n(n + 1) = 0 \tag{8}$$

with the roots

$$\varrho_1 = n, \quad \varrho_2 = -(n + 1). \tag{8'}$$

The two canonical solutions at this point therefore belong to the exponents n and $-(n + 1)$. Of these, since n is not negative, only the first is of use to us. Since it belongs to the *larger* exponent, it is represented by an ordinary power series beginning with r^n. (The other solution, which does not interest us, may contain a logarithm because of the integral difference between the exponents.) Since the next singular point is present only at infinity, the power series mentioned converges continuously and forms an *integral transcendental.* We therefore state:

The solution sought is an unambiguously (except for an unimportant constant factor) determined integral transcendental which belongs at $r = 0$ to the exponent n.

† For guidance in the treatment of Equation (7) I am greatly obliged to Hermann Weyl.

It is now a question of investigating the behaviour of this function at *infinity* on the positive real axis. For this purpose, we simplify Equation (7) by the substitution

$$\chi = r^{\alpha} U, \tag{9}$$

in which α is chosen in such a way that the term with $1/r^2$ vanishes. For this purpose, α must contain one of the two values n, $-(n + 1)$, as is easily checked by calculation. Equation (7) can assume the form:

$$\frac{d^2U}{dr^2} + \frac{2(\alpha + 1)}{r}\frac{dU}{dr} + \frac{2m}{K^2}\left(E + \frac{e^2}{r}\right)U = 0. \tag{7'}$$

Its solutions belong at $r = 0$ to the exponents 0 and $-2\alpha - 1$. For the first value of α, $\alpha = n$, the *first* of these solutions is an integral transcendental, and for the second value of α, $\alpha = -(n + 1)$, the *second* of them is and this leads according to (9) to the solution sought, which is unambiguous. We therefore lose nothing if we limit ourselves to *one* of the two values of α. We select

$$\alpha = n. \tag{10}$$

Our solution U therefore belongs at $r = 0$ to the exponent 0. Equation (7′) is called by mathematicians the Laplace equation. The general type is

$$U'' + \left(\delta_0 + \frac{\delta_1}{r}\right)U' + \left(\varepsilon_0 + \frac{\varepsilon_1}{r}\right)U = 0. \tag{7''}$$

In our case, the constants have the values

$$\delta_0 = 0, \quad \delta_1 = 2(\alpha + 1), \quad \varepsilon_0 = \frac{2mE}{K^2}, \quad \varepsilon_1 = \frac{2me^2}{K^2}. \tag{11}$$

This type of equation is comparatively easy to treat for *this* reason, that the so-called Laplace transformation which, in general, *again* gives an equation of the *second* order, *here* leads to the *first* order, which is soluble by quadratures. This permits a representation of the solution of (7″) itself by integrals in the complex domain. Here I give only the final result.† The integral

$$U = \int_L e^{zr}(z - c_1)^{\alpha_1 - 1} (z - c_2)^{\alpha_2 - 1}\, dz \tag{12}$$

is a solution of (7″) for an integration path L for which

$$\int_L \frac{d}{dz} [e^{zr}(z - c_1)^{\alpha_1} (z - c_2)^{\alpha_2}]\, dz = 0. \tag{13}$$

The constants $c_1, c_2, \alpha_1, \alpha_2$ have the following values: c_1 and c_2 are the roots of the quadratic equation

$$z^2 + \delta_0 z + \varepsilon_0 = 0 \tag{14}$$

and

$$\alpha_1 = \frac{\varepsilon_1 + \delta_1 c_1}{c_1 - c_2}, \quad \alpha_2 = \frac{\varepsilon_1 + \delta_1 c_2}{c_2 - c_1}. \tag{14′}$$

In the case of Equation (7′), therefore, from (11) and (10)

$$c_1 = +\sqrt{\frac{-2mE}{K^2}}, \quad c_2 = -\sqrt{\frac{-2mE}{K^2}};$$

$$\alpha_1 = \frac{me^2}{K\underset{+}{\sqrt{-2mE}}} + n + 1, \quad \alpha_2 = -\frac{me^2}{K\underset{+}{\sqrt{-2mE}}} + n + 1. \tag{14″}$$

The integral representation (12) does not only permit us to review the asymptotic behaviour of all the solutions when r goes to infinity in a certain manner, but also permits us to give this behaviour for a *definite* solution, which is always much more difficult.

We shall now first *exclude* the case in which α_1 and α_2 are real integers. The case always occurs, when it does occur, simultaneously for both quantities, in fact when and only when

$$\frac{me^2}{K\underset{+}{\sqrt{-2mE}}} = \text{a real integer.} \tag{15}$$

We now assume, therefore, that (15) is not satisfied.

† The theory is due to H. Poincaré and J. Horn.

The behaviour of the solutions when r becomes infinite in a certain way—we shall always think of a real positive process of becoming infinite—is then† characterized by the behaviour of the two linearly independent solutions that are obtained by the following *two specializations* of the integration path L and which we shall call U_1 and U_2. In *both* cases z comes from infinity and goes back to it along the same path, in such a direction that

$$\lim_{z=\infty} e^{zr} = 0, \tag{16}$$

i.e. the real part of zr will become negatively infinite. This satisfies the condition (13). *Between them* in the *one* case (solution U_1) the position c_1 and in the *other* case (solution U_2) the position c_2 is encircled once.

These two solutions are now represented *asymptotically* (in Poincaré's sense) for very large real positive values of r by

$$\begin{aligned} U_1 &\sim e^{c_1 r} r^{-\alpha_1} (-1)^{\alpha_1} (e^{2\pi i \alpha_1} - 1)\, \Gamma(\alpha_1)\, (c_1 - c_2)^{\alpha_2 - 1}, \\ U_2 &\sim e^{c_2 r} r^{-\alpha_2} (-1)^{\alpha_2} (e^{2\pi i \alpha_2} - 1)\, \Gamma(\alpha_2)\, (c_2 - c_1)^{\alpha_1 - 1}, \end{aligned} \tag{17}$$

where we restrict ourselves here to the first term of the asymptotic series in negative integral powers of r.

We now have to distinguish the two cases $E \gtrless 0$.

1. $E > 0$. We note in the first place that this by itself ensures that (15) does not apply, since this quantity becomes purely imaginary. Moreover, according to (14″) c_1 and c_2 become purely imaginary. Since r is real, the exponential functions in (17) are therefore finite periodic functions. The values of α_1 and α_2 according to (14″) show that U_1 and U_2 *both* tend to zero like r^{-n-1}. *The same must therefore apply to our integral transcendental solution* U, the behaviour of which we are seeking, since it can always be constructed linearly from U_1 and U_2. Furthermore (9) shows, in view of (10), that the function χ, i.e. the integral transcendental solution of the *original* Equation (7),

† When (15) is satisfied, at least one of the two paths of integration described in the text is unusable, since it gives a vanishing result.

always tends to zero like $1/r$, since it arises from U by multiplication by r^n. We can therefore state:

The Euler differential equation (5) *of our variational problem has solutions for each positive value of E that are single-valued, finite and continuous in the whole of space and at infinity, with continuous oscillations, tend to zero as 1/r.* The surface condition (6) will be discussed later.

2. $E < 0$. In this case, the possibility (15) is not *ipso facto* excluded but provisionally we take it as excluded by agreement. Then, according to (14″) and (17), U_1 for $r = \infty$ rises above all limits, while U_2 vanishes *exponentially*. Our integral transcendental U (and the same applies to χ) will therefore remain finite when and only when U is identical with U_2 except for a numerical factor. *But this is not the case.* This is shown as follows: if in (12) for the integration path L we chose a *closed* circuit round *both* points c_1 and c_2, which circuit is then *actually closed* on the Riemann surface of the integrand because *the sum* $\alpha_1 + \alpha_2$ is an integer, and therefore the condition (13) is satisfied *ipso facto*, it can easily be shown that the integral (12) then represents *our integral transcendental U*. In fact, it can be expanded in a series of positive powers of r which always converges for sufficiently small r, and therefore satisfies the differential equation (7′) and hence must coincide with that for U. Thus: U is represented by (12) when L is a closed circuit around both points c_1 and c_2. This closed circuit can, however, be so distorted that it appears to be *additively combined* from the two integration paths previously considered, belonging to U_1 and U_2 and, indeed, *with non-vanishing factors*, such as 1 and $e^{2\pi i\alpha_1}$. Consequently, U cannot coincide with U_2 but must also contain U_1. Q.E.D.

Our integral transcendental U, which alone of the solutions of (7′) comes into consideration for the solution of the problem, therefore does *not* remain finite for large values of r under the conditions laid down. With reservations with respect to the investigation of *completeness*, i.e. the proof that our process permits *all* linearly independent solutions of the problem to be discovered, we may therefore state:

For negative values of E which do not satisfy condition (15) *our variational problem has no solution.*

We now have to investigate that discrete family of negative values of E that *satisfy condition* (15). Then α_1 and α_2 are both integral. Of the two integration paths which the fundamental system U_1, U_2 gave us previously, the first must certainly be modified in order to yield a non-vanishing quantity. Since $\alpha_1 - 1$ is certainly positive, the position c_1 is therefore now neither a branch point nor a pole of the integrand but an ordinary zero. The position c_2 may also become regular if, in fact, $\alpha_2 - 1$ is also not negative. In *any* case, however, two suitable integration paths can easily be given and the integration can be carried out on them in closed form by means of known functions so that the behaviour of the solutions can be surveyed completely.

Let, in fact

$$\frac{me^2}{K\sqrt{-2mE}} = l; \qquad l = 1, 2, 3, 4, \ldots \tag{15'}$$

Then according to (14″)

$$\alpha_1 - 1 = l + n, \qquad \alpha_2 - 1 = -l + n. \tag{14''}$$

We now have to distinguish the two cases $l \leqq n$ and $l > n$.

(a) $l \leqq n$. Then c_2 and c_1 lose every singular character, but in exchange acquire the property of being suitable for functioning as starting points or end-points of the integration path for the purpose of satisfying condition (13). A third suitable point for this is the negative real infinite point. Every path between two of these three points yields a solution, and of these three solutions two are linearly independent, as can easily be confirmed by calculating the solutions in closed form. In particular, the *integral transcendental solution* is provided by the integration path from c_1 to c_2, for the fact that *this* integral remains regular for $r = 0$ can be seen directly without calculation. I stress this, since the actual calculation is rather suitable for masking this state of affairs. On the other hand, *it* shows that the solution increases above all bounds for positively infinite large values of r. One of the *other* two solutions remains *finite* for large values of r, but it becomes infinite for $r = 0$.

Consequently, in the case $l \leqq n$ we obtain *no* solution of the problem.

(b) $l > n$. Here, according to (14‴), c_1 is a zero and c_2 a pole of at least first order of the integrand. Two independent solutions are then given: one by the path which leads from $z = -\infty$ to the zero, avoiding the pole as a precaution; the other through the *residue* in the pole. The *latter* is the integral transcendental. We will give its calculated value, but multiplied by r^n, whereby through (9) and (10) we obtain the solution χ of the original Equation (7). (The unimportant multiplicative constant is adjusted arbitrarily.) We find:

$$\chi = f\left(r\frac{\sqrt{-2mE}}{K}\right); \quad f(x) = x^n e^{-x} \sum_{k=0}^{l-n-1} \frac{(-2x)^k}{k!} \binom{l+n}{l-n-1-k}. \tag{18}$$

It can be seen that this is actually a usable solution, since it remains finite for all real non-negative values of r. Moreover, because of its exponential vanishing at infinity the surface condition (6) is guaranteed. We summarize the results for negative values of E as follows:

For negative values of E, our variational problem has solutions when and only when E satisfies condition (15). *The integer n, which gives the order of the spherical harmonic appearing in the solution, may then always be given only values smaller than l (of which at least one is always available). The part of the solution dependent on r is given by* (18).

By counting off the constants in the spherical harmonics ($2n + 1$, as is well known), we also find:

The solution found contains, for a permissible (n, l) *combination exactly* $2n + 1$ *arbitrary constants; for a given value of l, it therefore contains* l^2 *arbitrary constants.*

In this way we have confirmed the statements given at the beginning on the eigenvalue spectrum of our variational problem in its main lines, although some gaps still exist. In the first place there is the proof of the completeness of the *whole* system of eigenfunctions found. I shall not deal with this here. According to experience in other fields, it may be assumed that no eigenvalues have escaped us.

In the second place, it must now be remembered that the eigenfunctions found for positive E do not immediately solve the variational problem in the form in which it was posed in the beginning, since at infinity it tends towards zero only as $1/r$, so that $\frac{\partial \psi}{\partial r}$ on a large sphere only vanishes as $1/r^2$. The surface integral (6) therefore still remains just of the order of the $\delta\psi$ at infinity. If, therefore, we actually wish to obtain the continuous spectrum as well, the *problem* must be supplemented by a condition: for instance, that $\delta\psi$ vanishes at infinity or, at least, that it must tend towards a constant value independent of the direction in which one goes in space to infinity; in the latter case, the spherical harmonics cause the surface integral to disappear.

§ **2.** The condition (15) gives

$$-E_l = \frac{me^4}{2K^2l^2}. \tag{19}$$

This therefore gives the well-known Bohr energy levels which correspond to the Balmer terms if the constant K, which we had to introduce into (2) for dimensional reasons, is given the value

$$K = \frac{h}{2\pi}. \tag{20}$$

Then, in fact,

$$-E_l = \frac{2\pi^2 me^2}{h^2l^2}. \tag{19'}$$

Our l is the principal quantum number. $n + 1$ is analogous to the azimuthal quantum number and the further resolution of this number in the more accurate determination of the spherical harmonics can be brought into analogy with the resolution of the azimuthal quantum number into an "equatorial" and a "polar" quantum number. *Here,* these figures determine the system of node lines on the sphere. The "radial quantum number" $l-n-1$ also accurately determines the number of "nodal spheres", since it is easily possible to be convinced that the function $f(x)$ in (18) has exactly $l - n - 1$ positive real roots. The positive values of E correspond to the continuum of the hyperbolic paths to which in the usual sense the radial quantum number ∞ can be ascribed. To this corresponds the fact that, as we have seen, the appropriate solutions go to infinity with *continuous* oscillations.

Also of interest is the fact that the range within which the functions (18) are appreciably different from zero and within which their oscillations take place is in any case of the *general order of magnitude* of the major axis of the associated ellipse. The factor by which the radius vector appears as argument of the constant-free function f is—obviously—the reciprocal of a length, and this length is

$$\frac{K}{\sqrt{-2mE}} = \frac{K^2 l}{me^2} = \frac{h^2 l}{4\pi^2 me^2} = \frac{a_l}{l}, \tag{21}$$

where a_l is the semi-axis of the l-th elliptical orbital. (The equations follow from (19) together with the well-known relation $E_l = -\dfrac{e^2}{2a_l}$). The quantity (21) gives the order of magnitude of the range of the roots for small values of l and n, since it may be assumed that the roots of $f(x)$ are of the order of magnitude of unity. This is of course no longer the case when the coefficients of the polynomial are large numbers. I cannot now go into a more accurate estimate of the roots, but I believe that this would confirm the above statement fairly accurately.

PAPER 3

Quantization as an Eigenvalue Problem†

E. Schrödinger

(Second Communication)‡

§ 1. The Hamiltonian Analogy between Mechanics and Optics

Before we go into the question of treating the eigenvalue problem of the quantum theory for other special systems, we shall elucidate more clearly the *general* relationship that exists between the Hamiltonian partial differential equation (H.E.) of a mechanical problem and the "associated" *wave equation*, i.e. in the case of the Kepler problem Equation (5) of the first communication. We had provisionally described this relation only briefly in accordance with its external analytical structure through the transformation (2), in itself incomprehensible, and the likewise incomprehensible transition from *setting an expression to zero* to the requirement that the *space integral of* the particular expression shall be *stationary*.§

† *Annalen der Physic*, **79**, 489, 1926.

‡ See these *Annalen*, **79**, p. 361 (1926) (this volume p. 94). For comprehension, it is *not* unconditionally necessary to read the first communication *before* the second.

§ This process of calculation is *not followed further* in the present communication. It is intended to serve only for the preliminary rough orientation with respect to the relationship between the wave equation and the H.E. The function ψ has not actually the relationship stated by Equation (2) of the first communication with the action function of a given motion. On the other hand, the relationship of the wave equation and the variational problem is obviously real to the highest degree: the integrand of the stationary integral is the Lagrangian for the wave process.

The *intrinsic* relationship of the Hamiltonian theory to the process of wave propagation is by no means new. It was not only well known to Hamilton himself but formed the starting point for his theory of mechanics, which grew out of his work on optically inhomogeneous media.† The Hamiltonian variational principle can be regarded as Fermat's *principle* for a wave propagation in configuration space (q space) and the H.E. states Huyghens' *principle* for this wave propagation. Unfortunately, in most modern accounts, these forceful and fruitful ideas of Hamilton's have been deprived of their beautiful intuitive clothing as a superfluous accessory in favour of a more colourless account of the analytical relations.‡

Let us consider the general problem of classical mechanics of conservative systems. The complete H.E. is

$$\frac{\partial W}{\partial t} + T\left(q_k, \frac{\partial W}{\partial q_k}\right) + V(q_k) = 0. \tag{1}$$

W is the action function, i.e. the time integral of the Lagrangian $T-V$ along a path of a system as a function of the final position and the time. q_k is a representant of the position coordinates, T is the kinetic energy as a function of the position and momentum coordinates, a quadratic form of the latter for which, as prescribed, the partial differential quotients of W with respect to the q_k are inserted. V is the potential energy. To solve the equation, we make the substitution

$$W = -Et + S(q_k), \tag{2}$$

† Cf., for example, E. T. Whittaker, *Analytical Dynamics*, Chapter 11.

‡ Since the summer of 1891, Felix Klein in his lectures on mechanics has repeatedly developed Jacobi's theory from quasi-optical considerations in higher non-Euclidean spaces. Cf. F. Klein, *Jahresber. d. Deutsch. Math. Ver.* **1**, 1891, and *Ztschr. f. Math. u. Phys.* **46**, 1901 (Ges.-Abb. II, pp. 601 and 603). In the second note, Klein states with slight reproach that his lecure before the meeting of scientists at Halle, in which, ten years previously, he had given an account of these relationships and had stressed the great importance of Hamilton's optical papers, "had not found the general acceptance that I had in view for it". I owe the reference to F. Klein to a friendly letter from Prof. Sommerfeld.

whereupon it is transformed to

$$2T\left(q_k, \frac{\partial W}{\partial q_k}\right) = 2(E - V). \tag{1'}$$

E is a first, arbitrary, integration constant and, as is known, denotes the energy of the system. In contrast to the usual custom, in (1′) we have permitted the function W itself to remain instead of, as is customary, writing in the time-free coordinate function S. This is a pure external feature.

The statement of Equation (1′) can now be made in the simplest manner by making use of Heinrich Hertz's terminology. Like all geometrical statements in the configuration space (space of the variables q_k) it becomes particularly simple and clear if by means of the kinetic energy of the system a non-Euclidean definition of measure is introduced into this space. Let $\bar{T}$ be the kinetic energy as a function of the *velocities* $\dot{q}_k$, and not, as above, of the *momenta*, then we put for the line element

$$ds^2 = 2\bar{T}(q_k, \dot{q}_k)\, dt^2. \tag{3}$$

The right-hand side contains dt only apparently; it indicates (through $\dot{q}_k\, dt = dq_k$) a quadratic form of the dq_k.

After this definition, we can, as is well known, make just the same simple use of such concepts as the angle of two line elements, perpendicularity, the divergence and rotation of a vector, the gradient of a scalar, the Laplace operator (= div grad) on a scalar, and so on, as in three-dimensional Euclidean space and we can with impunity make use of the Euclidean three-dimensional concept for the purposes of thought, except that the analytical expressions for these concepts become very slightly more complicated since in place of the Euclidean line elements the line elements (3) have to appear throughout. *We stipulate that in the following all geometrical statements in q space must be understood in this non-Euclidean sense.*

One of the most important changes for calculations is that we must carefully distinguish between covariant and contravariant components of a vector or tensor. But this complication is no greater than is already present in the case of skew cartesian axes.

The dq_k are the prototype of a contravariant vector. The coefficients of the form $2\bar{T}$ depending on the q_k therefore have covariant character and form the covariant fundamental tensor. $2T$ is the contravariant form associated with $2\bar{T}$, since the momentum coordinates, as is well known, form the covariant vector associated with the velocity vector $\dot{q}_k$, and the momentum is the velocity vector in covariant form. Now the left-hand side of (1′) is nothing other than the contravariant fundamental form in which the $\partial W/\partial q_k$ have been entered as variables. The latter form the components of the vector, covariant in accordance with its nature,

$$\text{grad } W.$$

This is therefore the meaning of expressing the kinetic energy in the momenta rather than in the velocities, namely, that we can only introduce covariant vector components into a contravariant form if something meaningful, i.e. invariant, will result.)

Equation (1′) therefore coincides with the simple statement

$$(\text{grad } W)^2 = 2(E - V) \tag{1''}$$

or

$$|\text{grad } W| = \sqrt{2(E - V)}\,. \tag{1'''}$$

This requirement is easy to analyze. Let us assume that a function W (of the form (2)) has been found which satisfies this requirement. Then this function can always be visualized for a definite t if in the q-space the family of surfaces $W =$ const. is drawn and its W value is written in for each one.

Now, on the one hand, as we shall immediately show, Equation (1‴) is an accurate prescription for the successive construction from any one surface of this family, *when it and its W value is known*, of all other surfaces and their W values. On the other hand, the only datum necessary for this construction, namely the *one* surface and its W value, can be *prescribed completely arbitrarily* and then be supplemented according to the directions for construction in just two ways to give a function W satisfying the requirement. In all this, we provisionally consider the time constant. Thus, the prescription for construction *exhausts* the content of the differential equation, and *each* of its solutions can be obtained from a surface plus W value taken suitably.

Now to the prescription for construction. Let therefore (see Fig. 1) the value W_0 be prescribed on an arbitrary surface. In order to find the surface which belongs to the value $W_0 + dW_0$, denote *one* side of the given surface arbitrarily as the positive one and let us erect the perpendicular at any point of the surface and lay off on it (taking account of the sign of dW_0) the *distance*

$$ds = \frac{dW_0}{\sqrt{2(E - V)}}. \tag{4}$$

The end-points of the perpendicular fall on the surface $W_0 + dW_0$. Continuing in this way the family of sufaces can be constructed successively towards both sides.

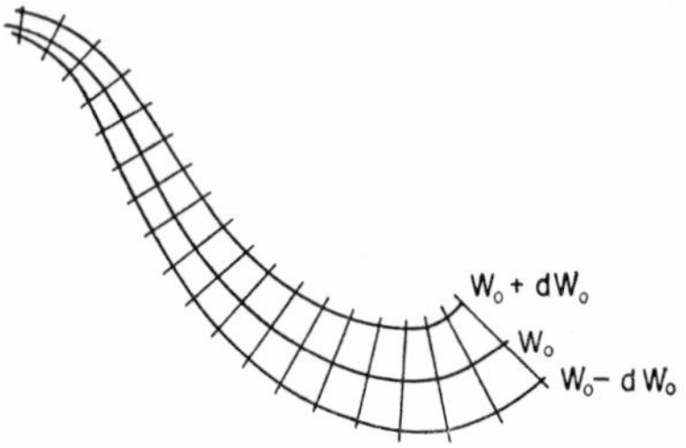

FIG. 1.

The construction is *ambiguous*, since before the first step we could have taken the *other* side as the positive one. However, for the later steps this ambiguity no longer exists, i.e. at any later stage of the process it is impossible to change over the designation of the side of the surface that we have just reached, since this would in general involve a discontinuity of the first differential quotients of W. Moreover, the two families of surfaces at which we arrive in the two cases are obviously identical, the only difference being that the W values ascribed to them run in opposite directions.

If we now consider the simplest possible dependence on the *time*, Equation (2) shows that at any later (or earlier) moment $t + t'$, as well, the *specific* family of surfaces shows the W distribution, with the only difference that other W values must be ascribed to the individual surfaces, namely by subtracting Et' from each of the W values given at time t. The W values migrate, so to speak, according to a certain simple law from surface to surface—in the case of positive E in the direction of increasing W values. Instead of this, it can be imagined that the *surfaces* migrate forwards, each taking the form and position of the subsequent one, and thereby *carry* their W values *with them*. The law of migration of the surfaces is given by the fact that, for example, at time $t + dt$ the surface W_0 must have reached that position which the surface $W_0 + E\,dt$ occupied at time t. This is achieved according to (4) by allowing each point of the surface W_0 to migrate in the direction of the positive perpendicular by

$$ds = \frac{E\,dt}{\sqrt{2(E - V)}}, \tag{5}$$

i.e. the surfaces move with a *normal velocity*

$$u = \frac{ds}{dt} = \frac{E}{\sqrt{2(E - V)}}, \tag{6}$$

which after the constant E has been prescribed is a pure position function.

We now see that our system of surfaces $W = \text{const.}$ can be regarded as the system of wave surfaces of an advancing but stationary wave movement in q-space for which the magnitude of the space velocity at each point of the space is given by (6), since the perpendicular construction can obviously be replaced by the construction of Huyghens' elementary waves [with the radius (5)] and their envelope. The "refractive index" is proportional to the reciprocal of (6); it depends on the position but not on the direction. The q-space is therefore optically inhomogeneous but isotropic. The elementary waves are spheres, although—as may be stated expressly here once more—spheres in the sense of the line element (3).

The action function W plays the role of the *phase* for our wave system. The H.E. is the expression of Huyghens' principle. If Fermat's principle is formulated

$$0 = \delta \int_{P_1}^{P_2} \frac{ds}{u} = \delta \int_{P_1}^{P_2} \frac{ds \sqrt{2(E-V)}}{E} = \delta \int_{t_1}^{t_2} \frac{2T}{E} dt = \frac{1}{E} \delta \int_{t_1}^{t_2} 2T \, dt, \tag{7}$$

we are led directly to the Hamiltonian principle in Maupertuis' form (where the time integrals are to be taken with the usual grain of salt, i.e. $T + V = E =$ const., even in the variation). The "rays", i.e. the orthogonal trajectories of the wave surfaces are therefore *paths* of the system of the energy value E, in agreement with the well known system of equations

$$p_k = \frac{\partial W}{\partial q_k}, \tag{8}$$

which states that from any special action function a family of system paths can be derived in the same way as a current from its velocity potential.† (The momenta p_k in fact simply form the covariant velocity vector, and Equations (8) state that it is equal to the gradients of the action function.)

Although in the above arguments we have spoken of wave surfaces, velocity of propagation, and Huyghens' principle, these must in fact be regarded not as an analogy of mechanics with *wave* optics but with *geometrical* optics, for the concept of *rays* which is mainly that which applies to mechanics, belongs to *geometrical* optics; it is only a clear concept for *this*. Fermat's principle can also be regarded from the point of view of pure

† See, in particular, A. Einstein, *Verh. d. D. Physik. Ges.* **19**, pp. 77, 82 (1917). Of all the modified forms of the quantum conditions, that given there is closest to that of the present paper. De Broglie has also gone back to them.

geometrical optics using only the concept of refractive index. And the system of W surfaces regarded as wave surfaces is in somewhat looser relationship to mechanical motion in so far as the image point of the mechanical system on the ray does not by any means advance with the wave velocity, for instance, but, on the contrary, its velocity is (at constant E) proportional to $1/u$. It is in fact found directly from (3) as

$$v = \frac{ds}{dt} = \sqrt{2T} = \sqrt{2(E - V)}\,. \tag{9}$$

This non-agreement is illuminating. In the first place, according to (8): the system point velocity is *high* where grad W is large, i.e. where the W surfaces are closely packed, i.e. where u is small. In the second place from the significance as W as time integral of the Lagrangian: this naturally *changes* during the movement [during dt by $(T - V)\,dt$]; consequently the image point *can* not remain continuously in contact with the same W surface.

And therefore even important concepts of wave theory, such as amplitude, wavelength, frequency—or, speaking generally, the wave *form*—do not appear at all in the analogy and there are no mechanical parallels to them; nothing is said of the wave function itself and W for the wave has only the significance of *phase*—actually somewhat blurred in view of the uncertainty of the wave *form*.

If the whole parallel is regarded as nothing more than a gratifying means of representation, this effect is in no way disadvantageous and the attempt to eliminate it will be felt as idle play; the analogy *exists just* with *geometrical* optics or, if you like, with a very primitive wave optics, and not with the fully developed wave optics. Since geometrical optics is only a rough approximation for *light*, nothing is changed in this. In the further development of the q-space optics in the sense of the wave theory it will be necessary, to *maintain* the analogy, to take care precisely that we do not depart considerably from the limiting case of geometrical optics; perhaps by choosing the *wavelength* sufficiently small†—small as compared with all path dimensions. Then, however, the added matter teaches nothing new and it decks out the picture only with superfluous matter.

This may be thought at first sight. But even the first attempt at the shaping of a wave theory leads to such striking things that quite a different suspicion arises: *we know even today that our classical mechanics fails with very small orbital dimensions and very pronounced orbital curvatures.* This failure is perhaps a complete analogy with the failure of geometrical optics, i.e. the "optics with infinitely small wavelengths" which, as is well known, occurs as soon as the "obstacles" or "apertures" are no longer large compared with the actual finite wavelengths. Perhaps our classical mechanics is the *complete* analogue of geometrical optics and, as such, erroneous and not in agreement with reality; it fails as soon as the radii of curvature and dimensions of the orbit are no longer large as compared with a certain wavelength to which real significance is attached in the q-space. Then it is a case of seeking an "undulatory mechanics"‡—and the most obvious route to this is in fact the form of the Hamiltonian picture based on the wave theory.

§ 2. "Geometrical" and "Undulatory" Mechanics

We first make the assumption that there is an appropriate construction of the analogy of considering the wave system considered above as *sine* waves. This is the simplest and most obvious assumption, but the *arbitrariness* that it contains must be stressed because of the *fundamental importance* of this assumption. The wave function will therefore contain the time only in

† For the optical case, see A. Sommerfeld and Iris Runge, *Ann. d. Phys.* **35**, p. 290 (1911). It is shown there (developing an oral remark by P. Debye) how the equation of the *first* order and *second* degree for the *phase* ("Hamiltonian equation") can be derived accurately from the equation of the *second* order and *first* degree for the wave function ("wave equation") in the limiting case of vanishing wavelengths.

‡ Cf. A. Einstein, *Berl. Ber.*, pp. 9ff. (1925).

the form of a factor sin (.....) the argument of which is a linear function of W. The coefficient of W must, since W, an action, is the phase of a sine but an unknown number, have the dimensions of a reciprocal action. We assume that it is universal, i.e. not simply independent of E but also of the nature of the mechanical system. We may in fact immediately denote it by $2\pi/h$. The time factor therefore reads

$$\sin\left(\frac{2\pi W}{h} + \text{const}\right) = \sin\left(-\frac{2\pi Et}{h} + \frac{2\pi S(q_k)}{h} + \text{const}\right). \tag{10}$$

Consequently, the *frequency* ν of the waves is found to be

$$\nu = \frac{E}{h}. \tag{11}$$

The frequency of the q-space waves is thus found to be proportional to the energy of the system without appreciable artificiality.† This is obviously only meaningful when E is determined absolutely and not, as in classical mechanics, determined except for an additive constant. The *wavelength* according to (6) and (11) is *independent* of this additive constant

$$\lambda = \frac{u}{\nu} = \frac{h}{\sqrt{2(E - V)}}, \tag{12}$$

since the radicand is double the kinetic energy. If we make a very preliminary rough comparison of this wavelength with the dimensions of the orbit of a hydrogen electron as given by classical mechanics, it can be seen that because of (3) a "distance" in our q-space does not have the dimensions of a length but of length times $\sqrt{\text{mass}}$. λ has the same dimensions. Consequently, we must, as can easily be seen, divide λ by the dimensions of the orbit, let us say a (cm), times the square root of the

† In the first communication, this relation appeared merely as an approximate equation within the framework of a pure speculation.

electron mass m. The quotient is to an order of magnitude

$$\frac{h}{mva},$$

where v is for the moment the velocity of the electron (cm/sec^{-1}). The denominator mva has the order of magnitude of the mechanical angular momentum. The fact that for Kepler orbits of atomic dimensions this is at least of the order of magnitude of 10^{-27} follows, before any quantum theory, from the known values of the electronic charge and mass. We therefore in fact actually obtain the right order of magnitude for the *limit of the approximate range of validity of classical mechanics* when we identify our constant h with Planck's quantum of action. This is only for preliminary orientation.

If in (6) E is expressed in accordance with (11), we obtain

$$u = \frac{h\nu}{\sqrt{2(h\nu - V)}}. \qquad (6')$$

The dependence of the wave velocity on the energy of the system therefore becomes a peculiar dependence on the frequency, i.e. on a *dispersion law* for the waves. This dispersion law is of great interest. In § 1 we have referred to the fact that the migrating wave surfaces are in a loose relationship with the movement of the point of the system to the extent that the velocities are not equal and cannot be equal. According to (9), (11), and (6′), the system velocity v now has a very concrete significance even for the waves. It is immediately confirmed that

$$v = \frac{d\nu}{d\left(\frac{\nu}{u}\right)}, \qquad (13)$$

i.e. the velocity of the point of the system is that of a *wave group* which has a small frequency range (signal velocity). Here we find once again a law that de Broglie had derived in his elegant investigations,† to which I owe the inspiration of this work,

† L. de Broglie, *Annales de Physique* (10) **3**, p. 22 (1925) (Thèses, Paris, 1924) (for abstracts see this volume, p. 79).

for the "phase waves" of the electron, with particular reference to the theory of relativity. It can be seen that this is a theorem of great generality, which does not arise from the theory of relativity but also applies to any conservative system of ordinary mechanics.

This fact can now be made use of to produce a much more intimate connection between wave propagation and representative point movement than appeared previously. An attempt can be made to construct a wave group which has relatively small dimensions in all directions. Such a wave group will then probably follow the same laws of motion as an individual representative point of the mechanical system. It can, so to speak, represent a *substitute* of the representative point as long as it can be regarded as approximately point-like, i.e. as long as its extension can be neglected as compared with the dimensions of the system path. However, this will only be the case when the path dimensions, particularly the radii of curvature of the path, are very large compared with the wavelength since, by analogy with ordinary optics, it is clear beforehand that the dimensions of the wave group can not only not be reduced below the order of magnitude of the wavelength but that, on the contrary, the group must extend in all directions over a large number of wavelengths if it is to be *approximately monochromatic*. We must demand this, however, since the wave group must travel as a whole with definite group velocity and correspond to a mechanical system of definite energy (see Equation (11)).

. . . . .

What I now suspect with great conviction is the following:

The actual mechanical phenomenon is comprised in an appropriate manner or represented by the *wave processes* in q-space and not by the motion of representative *points* in this space. The study of the motion of representative points, which forms the subject of classical mechanics, is only an approximate process and as such has exactly the same justification as geometrical or ray optics in comparison with the true optical processes. A macroscopic mechanical process will have to be imagined as a wave signal of the type described above which can be regarded with sufficient approximation as point-like in comparison with the geometrical structure of the trajectory. We have seen that in this case of such a signal or wave group just the same laws of motion in fact hold as are given by classical mechanics for the representative point. This method of treatment loses all meaning, however, when the path structure is no longer very large as compared with the wavelengths or is even comparable with it. Then the strict wave-theoretical treatment *must* come in, i.e. in order to make a picture of the multiplicity of the possible processes, we must start from the *wave equation* and not from the basic equations of mechanics. The latter are also incapable of use for explaining the microstructure of the mechanical phenomenon, just as geometrical optics is incapable of use for explaining *diffraction phenomena.*

If some explanation at all of this microstructure in connection with classical mechanics has been arrived at—obviously with very artificial additional assumptions—and has shown practical successes of the highest significance, it appears to me very significant that this theory—I mean the quantum theory in the form preferred by Sommerfeld, Schwarzschild, Epstein *et al.*—is in extremely intimate relation with just the H.E. and the Hamilton–Jacobi solution theory, i.e. with that form of classical mechanics which in fact contains the clearest indication of the true undulatory nature of the mechanical phenomenon. In fact, the H.E. corresponds to Huyghens' principle (in its older simple form and not in the strict Kirchhoff form). And as this, supplemented by some ideas quite incomprehensible to the worker in geometrical optics (Fresnel zone construction), already does justice to the diffraction phenomena to a large extent, so light could be thrown on the processes in the atom from the theory of the action function. On the other hand, we must have become involved in insoluble contradiction if we—as was obviously very natural—attempted to maintain the concept of *system paths* for these atomic processes also, just as we lose ourselves in unintelligibilities if we attempt to trace the course of *light rays* in the field of a diffraction phenomenon.

. . . . .

It is in *this* sense that I explain the "phase waves" accompanying the path of the electron according to de Broglie—in the sense, that is, that, at least in atomic structures, no outstanding importance is attached to the orbit of the electron itself and still less to the position of the electron in its orbit. And in this sense do I explain the conviction which is beginning to break through more and more at the present time, *firstly*: that real importance must be ascribed to the *phase* of the electron motions in the atom; *secondly*: that we can never state that the electron is present at a certain instant *in a definite* one of the quantum orbits specified by the quantum conditions; and *thirdly*: that the true laws of quantum mechanics consist not in particular specifications for the *individual orbit*, but that these true laws combine the elements of the whole multiplicity of orbits of a system connected by equations so that a certain interaction between the various orbits apparently exists.†

It is not incomprehensible that a careful analysis of the experimental data must lead to statements of this kind if the experimental data are the result of such a structure of the actual phenomenon as we are dealing with here. All these statements in fact contribute systematically to the resolution of the concept "electron position" and "electron orbit", and if we do not decide on this resolution, they remain contradictory. This contradiction is so strongly felt that it has been doubted whether the phenomena in the atom can be included in the space-time form of thought at all. From the philosophic point of view, I would regard a definitive decision in this sense as equivalent to a complete surrender, since we know that the forms of thought do not actually change and what we cannot understand within them

† Cf., particularly, recent papers by Heisenberg, Born, Jordan, and Dirac, and also N. Bohr, *Die Naturwissenschaften*, January 1926.

we cannot understand at all. Such things exist—but I do not believe that the structure of the atom belongs to them. From our point of view, however, there is in fact no reason for such doubt although, or, better, *because* its appearance is extraordinarily easy to understand. Thus, even a worker in geometrical optics who continually failed in his attempts to attack diffraction phenomena by means of the concept of rays that has proved valuable in macroscopic optics—even such a man, I say, at the very last might come to the opinion that the *laws of geometry* are not applicable to diffraction phenomena since he is continually led to the fact that the rays of light which to him are *rectilinear* and *independent* of one another now suddenly exhibit the most remarkable *curvatures* even in a homogeneous medium and obviously *mutually affect one another*. I consider this analogy to be *very* close. There is even an analogue in the atom to the unmotivated *curvatures*—one thinks of the "non-mechanical constraint" invented to explain the anomalous Zeeman effect.

In what way, now, do we have to proceed in the undulatory formulation of mechanics in those cases where it has proved necessary? Instead of the basic equations of mechanics we must start from a wave equation for q-space and consider the multiplicity of the processes possible *according to this*. In this communication, the wave equation has not yet been used explicitly and has not in fact yet been given. The only datum for its formulation is the *wave velocity* given by (6) or (6′) as a function of the mechanical energy parameter or the frequency, and this datum obviously does not determine the wave equation unambiguously. It is in fact not yet settled that it must be just of second order, and only a striving for simplicity provides an impulse for investigating the first. We shall then put for the wave function ψ

$$\text{div grad}\,\psi - \frac{1}{u^2}\ddot{\psi} = 0 \tag{18}$$

valid for processes which depend on the time only by a factor $e^{2\pi i\nu t}$. This means, therefore, taking (6), (6′), and (11) into account

$$\operatorname{div}\operatorname{grad}\psi + \frac{8\pi^2}{h^2}(h\nu - V)\psi = 0, \tag{18'}$$

or

$$\operatorname{div}\operatorname{grad}\psi + \frac{8\pi^2}{h^2}(E - V)\psi = 0. \tag{18''}$$

The differential operators are obviously to be understood with respect to the line element (3). But even with the second-order formulae this is not the only one compatible with (6): the generalization is possible in which div grad ψ is replaced by

$$f(q_k)\operatorname{div}\left(\frac{1}{f(q_k)}\operatorname{grad}\psi\right) \tag{19}$$

where f may be any desired function of the q_k which must obviously depend in some plausible manner on E, $V(q_k)$ and the coefficients of the line element (3) (one could think, for example, of $f = u$). Our formula is again dictated by the striving for simplicity, but in this case I consider that an error cannot be excluded.†

The substitution of a *partial* differential equation as a replacement for the basic equations of dynamics for the problem of the atom now appears at first sight to be extraordinarily uncertain because of the enormous multiplicity of solutions satisfying such an equation. Even classical dynamics had led not to an excessively limited but to a much too extensive multiplicity of solutions—namely to a *continuous family*—while according to all experience only a discontinuous set of the solutions appeared to be realized. The task of the quantum theory is, according to the prevailing opinion, just that of separating out from the continuous family of the orbits possible according to classical mechanics the discrete family of those actually occurring by means of the "quantum conditions". It appears to be a poor beginning for a new attempt in this direction, therefore,

† The introduction of $f(q_k)$ means that not merely the "density" but also the "elasticity" varies with the position.

if it begins to *increase* the number of solutions, in accordance with their transcendental order of magnitude instead of reducing it.

In fact, the problem of classical dynamics can also be clad in the garb of a *partial* equation—namely just the H.E. But the multiplicity of the solutions of the problem does not correspond to the multiplicity of the solutions of the H.E. Any "complete" solution of the H.E. solves the mechanical problem *with no residue*, and any *other* complete solution gives the same orbits but in a different combination with respect to multiplicities of orbits.

Now as far as relates to the fear expressed in relation to Equation (18) as the basis of atomic dynamics, I will indeed not state that no other additional conditions must enter this equation. However, they will probably no longer have such a completely strange and incomprehensible character as previous "quantum conditions" but be of that type to which we are accustomed in physics in the case of a partial differential equation: as initial or boundary conditions. Thus, they will also in no way be *analogous* to the quantum conditions, since it is found in all cases of classical dynamics that I have investigated so far that Equation (18) *includes the quantum conditions within itself.* In certain cases —namely those in which experience indicates it—it *spontaneously* separates out certain frequencies or energy levels as the only ones possible for stationary processes without any additional assumption whatever other than the requirement for the function ψ, which is almost an obvious one for the physical quantity, that it shall be single-valued, finite and continuous over the whole of configuration space.

Consequently, I convert the fear expressed into its opposite, at least so far as concerns the energy levels or, let us say more carefully, the frequencies (for what the "energy of the vibrations" implies is a question in itself, and it must not be forgotten that it is just in the single-body problem that this is a case of something which immediately permits the explanation as vibrations in the true three-dimensional space). The determination of the quantum levels *no longer takes place* in two intimately separated steps: (1) determination of all the dynamically possible orbits; (2) rejection of the superfluous part of the solutions obtained under (1), and separation of a few of them by means of special requirements; on the contrary, the quantum levels are determined *once for all* as the *eigenvalues of Equation* (18) which *already include their natural boundary conditions.*

. . . . .

§ 3. Applications

We shall now add a few other examples to the Kepler problem treated in the first communication. These are only the very simplest, since provisionally we are limited to *classical* mechanics without a magnetic field.†

1. Planck's Oscillator. The Question of Degeneration

We first treat the one-dimensional oscillator. Let the coordinate q be the elongation multiplied by the square root of the mass. The two forms of the kinetic energy are then

$$\bar{T} = \tfrac{1}{2}\dot{q}^2, \qquad T = \tfrac{1}{2}p^2. \tag{20}$$

The potential energy is

$$V(q) = 2\pi^2\nu_0^2 q^2, \tag{21}$$

where ν_0 is the natural frequency in the mechanical sense. Then for this case, Equation (18) runs:

$$\frac{d^2\psi}{dq^2} + \frac{8\pi^2}{h^2}(E - 2\pi^2\nu_0^2 q^2)\,\psi = 0. \tag{22}$$

† In relativity mechanics and taking a magnetic field into account, the statements of the H.E. are more complicated. In the case of a single electron it states that the *four-dimensional* gradient of the action function *minus* a predetermined vector (the four-potential) is constant. The wave-theoretical translation of this statement offers certain difficulties.

For brevity let us write

$$a = \frac{8\pi^2 E}{h^2}, \qquad b = \frac{16\pi^4 \nu_0^2}{h^2} \tag{23}$$

therefore

$$\frac{d^2\psi}{dq^2} + (a - bq^2)\,\psi = 0. \tag{22'}$$

We introduce as independent variable

$$x = q\sqrt[4]{b} \tag{24}$$

and obtain

$$\frac{d^2\psi}{dx^2} + \left(\frac{a}{\sqrt{b}} - x^2\right)\psi = 0. \tag{22''}$$

The eigenvalues and eigenfunctions of this equation are *known*.† With the symbols used here, the eigenvalues are

$$\frac{a}{\sqrt{b}} = 1, 3, 5 \ldots (2n + 1) \ldots \tag{25}$$

The eigenfunctions are the *Hermitian orthogonal functions*

$$e^{-(x^2/2)} H_n(x). \tag{26}$$

$H_n(x)$ means the n-th Hermitian polynomial, which can be defined as

$$H_n(x) = (-1)^n \, e^{x^2} \frac{d^n e^{-x^2}}{dx^n} \tag{27}$$

or explicitly

$$H_n(x) = (2x)^n - \frac{n(n-1)}{1!}(2x)^{n-2} + \frac{n(n-1)(n-2)(n-3)}{2!}(2x)^{n-4} - \cdots \tag{27'}$$

† Cf. Courant-Hilbert, *Methoden der mathematischen Physik I* (Berlin Springer, 1924) V, § 9, p. 261, Eq. 43, and also II, § 10, 4, p. 76.

The first of these polynomials are

$$H_0(x) = 1 \qquad H_1(x) = 2x$$
$$H_2(x) = 4x^2 - 2 \qquad H_3(x) = 8x^3 - 12x$$
$$H_4(x) = 16x^4 - 48x^2 + 12 \quad . \; . \; . \; . \; . \; . \; . \; . \qquad (27'')$$

If we first consider the eigenvalues, from (25) and (23) we obtain

$$E_n = \frac{2n+1}{2} h\nu_0; \qquad n = 0, 1, 2, 3, \ldots \qquad (25')$$

The so-called "half-integral" multiples of the "energy quanta" characteristic of the oscillator, i.e. the *odd* multiples of $h\nu_0/2$, appear as quantum levels. The separations of the levels, which alone are decisive for the radiation, are the same as in the previous theory. Remarkably, our quantum levels are *exactly* the same as in Heisenberg's theory. For the theory of *specific heats*, this deviation from the previous theory is not without significance, but it first comes into play when, as a consequence of thermal expansion, the eigenfrequency ν_0 *varies*. Formally, it is the old question of the "zero-point energy", which had already appeared in connection with the dilemma: first or second form of Planck's theory. The additional term $h\nu_0/2$ also influences the law of the *band edges*.

The *eigenfunctions* (26) are, when the original quantity q is again introduced according to (24) and (23):

$$\psi_n(q) = e^{-(2\pi^2\nu_0 q^2/h)} H_n\left(2\pi q \sqrt{\frac{\nu_0}{h}}\right). \qquad (26')$$

A consideration of (27″) shows that the first eigenfunction is a "Gaussian error curve" and the second vanishes at the origin and corresponds for positive values of x to a "Maxwellian velocity distribution" in two dimensions which is continued non-linearly towards negative values of x. The third eigenfunction is again linear and is negative at the origin, and has two symmetrical zeroes $\pm 1/\sqrt{2}$; and so on. The qualitative shape can easily be seen and sketched, while it must be borne in mind that the roots of successive polynomials *separate* one another. It is known from (26′) that the characteristic points of the eigenfunctions such as the half-value breadth (for $n = 0$), zeroes, and maxima lie with respect to order of magnitude in the region of the classical oscillator vibration, since for the classical *amplitude* of the n-th vibration we easily find

$$q_n = \frac{\sqrt{E_n}}{2\pi\nu_0} = \frac{1}{2\pi}\sqrt{\frac{h}{\nu_0}}\sqrt{\frac{2n+1}{2}}. \tag{28}$$

However, as far as I can see, in general the *exact* value of the abscissa of the classical *reversal point* has no particular significance in the shape of the eigenfunction. Something like this could be assumed, since the reversal points have *that* significance for the phase space wave that it is there that the square of the velocity of propagation becomes *infinite* and at a greater distance it becomes *negative*. In the differential equation (22), however, this means only the *disappearance* of the coefficient of ψ and gives rise to no singularity whatever.

PAPER 4

On the Relationship of the Heisenberg–Born–Jordan Quantum Mechanics to Mine†

E. SCHRÖDINGER

§ 1. Introduction and Synopsis

In view of the extraordinary divergence of the starting points and concepts of Heisenberg's quantum mechanics,‡ on the one hand, and the theory recently given here in its basic outlines and called "undulatory" or "physical" mechanics,§ on the other hand, it is very strange that, with respect to the special results that have become known so far, these two new quantum theories *agree with one another* even where they differ from the old quantum theory. I mention particularly the peculiar "half-integer" in the oscillator and in the rotator. This is really very remarkable, since the starting point, concepts, method, and the whole mathematical apparatus in fact appear to be different. Above all, however, the departure from classical mechanics in the two

† *Annalen der Physik*, **79**, 734, 1926.

‡ W. Heisenberg, *Ztschr. f. Phys.* **33**, p. 879, 1935; M. Born and P. Jordan, *ibid.* **34**, p. 858, 1925, and **35**, p. 557, 1926 (the latter *with* Heisenberg). Below, for brevity, I permit myself in general to replace the three authors names by that of Heisenberg and cite the two last-mentioned papers as "Quantum mechanics I and II". Interesting contributions to the theory have also been made by P. Dirac, *Proc. Roy. Soc. London*, **109**, p. 642, 1925, and *ibid.* **110**, p. 561, 1926.

§ E. Schrödinger, *Ann. d. Phys.* **79**, p. 361 (1st Communication; reprinted in this volume on p. 94); **79**, p. 489, 1926 (2nd Communication; reprinted in this volume on p. 106). This series of communications will be continued, quite independent of the present Note which is intended only to represent the connection.

theories appears to take place in directions which are actually diametrically opposed. Heisenberg replaces the classical continuous variables by sets of discrete numerical quantities (matrices), which, depending on an integral index pair, are determined by *algebraic* equations. The authors themselves call the theory a "true discontinuum theory".† On the other hand, wave mechanics denotes just conversely a step away from classical mechanics to *the continuum theory.* In fact, in place of the phenomenon describable by a finite number of dependent variables through a finite number of total differential equations, a continuous *field* phenomenon in the configuration space that is governed by a single *partial* differential equation derivable from an action principle appears. This action principle, or this differential equation, replaces the equations of motion *and* the quantum conditions of the older "classical quantum theory".‡

Below we shall deal only with the very intimate *intrinsic relationship* of Heisenberg's quantum mechanics and my wave mechanics. From the formal mathematical standpoint, this must in fact be called an *identity* (of the two theories). The outline of the proof is as follows.

Heisenberg's theory links the solution of a problem of quantum mechanics to the resolution of a system of an infinite number of algebraic equations, the unknowns—infinite matrices—of which are assigned to the classical coordinates of position and momentum of the mechanical system and functions of them and follow peculiar *laws of calculation.* (The assignment is as follows: *one* position coordinate, *one* momentum coordinate, or *one* function of them always corresponds to *one* infinite matrix.)

† "Quantum mechanics I", p. 879.

‡ My theory was inspired by L. de Broglie, *Ann. de Physique* (10) **3**, p. 22, 1925 (Thèses, Paris, 1924, partly reprinted in this volume on p. 73) and by short but incomplete remarks by A. Einstein, *Berl. Ber.* (1925) pp. 9ff. No genetic relationship whatever with Heisenberg is known to me. I knew of his theory, of course, but felt discouraged, not to say repelled, by the methods of transcendental algebra, which appeared very difficult to me and by the lack of visualisability.

I shall first show (§§ 2 and 3) how a matrix can be assigned to each function of the position and momentum coordinates in such a way that these matrices *always satisfy* the Born–Heisenberg formal rules of calculation (among which I also include the so-called "quantum condition" or "commutation rule"; see below). This assignment of matrices to functions is *general*; it still has no reference at all to the *special* mechanical system which in fact is present, but is the same for all mechanical systems. (In other words: the special Hamiltonian function still does not occur in the assignment.) However, on the other hand, the correlation is still *undetermined* to a high degree. It is in fact carried out *by means* of an *arbitrary* complete orthogonal system of functions with as basic domain the "*complete configuration space*". (NB *not* "*pq*-space", but "*q*-space".) The provisional *indeterminacy* of the correlation resides just in the fact that the role of intermediate can be transferred to *any* orthogonal system.

After matrices that satisfy the general rules of calculation have been constructed in a very general manner in this way, in § 4 I shall show the following: the resolution of the *special* system of algebraic equations characteristic for the *special* problem which links the *matrices* of the position and momentum coordinates with the matrix of the Hamiltonian function and which the authors call "equations of motion" will be performed completely by transferring the role of intermediary to a *definite* orthogonal system, namely the system of the eigenfunctions of that partial differential equation which forms the basis of my wave mechanics. The solution of the natural *eigenvalue problem* of this differential equation is *completely equivalent* to the resolution of Heisenberg's algebraic problem. *All* Heisenberg's matrix elements in which there may be interest, perhaps on the assumption that they determine the "transition probabilities" or "line intensities", can in fact be calculated *by differentiations and quadratures*, as soon as the eigenvalue problem has been solved. Furthermore, these matrix elements, or quantities closely related to them, have an absolutely clear significance as amplitudes of the partial vibrations of the electric moment of the atom. The intensity and polarization of the emitted light can therefore be understood *on the basis of the Maxwell–Lorentz theory*. A short preliminary sketch of this relationship is given in § 5.

§ 2. The Assignment of an Operator and a Matrix to a Well-Arranged Function Symbol and the Confirmation of the Product Rule

The central point in the construction of the matrices consists in the simple observation that Heisenberg's peculiar laws of calculation for functions of the *twice n* quantities: q_1, q_2, q_n; p_1, p_2, p_n (position and canonically conjugated momentum coordinates) agree exactly with the laws of calculation that apply *in accordance with the usual analysis* for the *linear differential operators* in the field of the *once n* variables $q_1, q_2 \cdots q_n$. In this process, the correlation must be carried out in such a way that in the *function* each p_l is replaced by the operator $\partial/\partial q_l$. In fact, the operator $\partial/\partial q_l$ commutes with $\partial/\partial q_m$ for any m but with q_m only if $m \neq l$. The operator obtained for $m = l$ by transposition and subtraction,

$$\frac{\partial}{\partial q_l} q_l - q_l \frac{\partial}{\partial q_l}, \tag{1}$$

performed on any function of the q_k *reproduces* the function, i.e. this operator is the *identity*. This simple fact will be reproduced in the field of matrices as Heisenberg's commutation rule.

After these preliminary remarks for orientation, let us pass to the systematic structure. Because of the "incomplete commutability" just mentioned, a given "function in the usual sense" of the q_k, p_k does not correspond unambiguously to a definite operator but to a "function symbol written in a certain way". In addition, since we can undertake no other calculating operation with the operators $\partial/\partial q_k$ than addition and multiplication, the function of the q_k, p_k must be written as regular power series at least in the p_k, so that we can undertake the replacement of p_l by $\partial/\partial q_l$. It is sufficient to give the argument for a single member of such a power series, i.e. for a function of the following structure

$$F(q_k, p_k) = f(q_1 \dots q_n)\, p_r p_s p_t g(q_1 \dots q_n)\, p_{r'} h(q_1 \dots q_n)\, p_{r''} p_{s''} \dots \quad (2)$$

We shall call this a "well-ordered function symbol" and assign to it the following operator

$$[F, \cdot] = f(q_1 \dots q_n)\, K^3 \frac{\partial^3}{\partial q_r\, \partial q_s\, \partial q_t}$$
$$g(q_1 \dots q_n)\, K \frac{\partial}{\partial q_{r'}} h(q_1 \dots q_n)\, K^2 \frac{\partial^2}{\partial q_{r''}\, \partial q_{s''}} \dots, \quad (3)$$

in which, in a somewhat more general manner than in the rough preliminary remarks, p_r is replaced not simply by $\partial/\partial q_r$, but by $K \dfrac{\partial}{\partial q_r}$ and K is to denote a universal constant. As an abbreviation for the operator arising from the well-ordered function F, I have provisionally (i.e. only for the purpose of the present proof) introduced the symbol $[F, \cdot\,]$. By $[F, u]$ I shall denote that function (in the usual sense) of $q_1 \cdots q_n$ that is obtained when the operator is applied to a function (in the usual sense) $u(q_1 \cdots q_n)$. If G is another well-ordered function, $[GF, u]$ will denote the function u after the operator of F has been applied to it *first* and *then* that of G; or, which is the same thing according to definition, the operator of GF. Naturally, in general this is not the same as $[FG, u]$.

Now we assign a *matrix* to a well-ordered function, such as F, by means of its operator (3) and any complete orthogonal system with as domain the complete q-space, in the following way. For brevity, for the group of variables $q_1, q_2 \cdots q_n$ we shall write simply x, as is customary from the theory of integral equations, and $\int dx$ for an integral extending over the whole q-space. The functions

$$u_1(x)\sqrt{\varrho(x)}, \qquad u_2(x)\sqrt{\varrho(x)}, \qquad u_3(x)\sqrt{\varrho(x)}\dots \quad (4)$$

will now form a complete orthogonal system normalized to 1. In any case, therefore,

$$\left.\begin{aligned}\int \varrho(x)\, u_i(x)\, u_k(x)\, dx &= 0 \quad \text{for} \quad i \neq k,\\ &= 1 \quad \text{for} \quad i = k.\end{aligned}\right\} \tag{5}$$

Moreover, it will be assumed that these functions vanish in a sufficiently pronounced manner at the natural *boundary* of the q-space (in general, infinity) in order to cause the integrated parts occurring as by-products in the integrations by parts, to be undertaken later, to vanish.

We now assign the following *matrix* to the function F represented by (2) with the operator (3)

$$F^{kl} = \int \varrho(x)\, u_k(x)\, [F, u_l(x)]\, dx. \tag{6}$$

(The method of writing the left-hand index must not arouse the thought "contravariant"; from this point of view, which we leave on one side here, it will be better to write *one* index above and the other below; we write the matrix indices *above* since we later have to add the matrix elements corresponding to the q_k, p_k themselves, in which the lower position is occupied.) In words: a matrix element is calculated by *multiplying* the function of the orthogonal system denoted by the *row* index (by which we always mean the u_i and not the $u_i\sqrt{\varrho}$) by the "density function" ϱ and by the operator applied to the orthogonal function denoted by the column index, and *integrating* over the domain.†

It is not very difficult to show that additive and multiplicative combinations of the well-ordered functions or the associated operators act on the associated matrices as matrix addition and matrix multiplication. For the addition, this is trivial. For multiplication, the proof is as follows. Let G be any well-ordered function other than F, and

$$G^{lm} = \int \varrho(x)\, u_l(x)\, [G, u_m(x)]\, dx \tag{7}$$

† More briefly: F^{kl} is the k-th "expansion coefficient" of the operator applied to the function u_l.

the matrix assigned to it. We shall form the product matrix

$$(FG)^{km} = \sum_l F^{kl} G^{lm}$$

Before we write it, we form the expression (6) for F^{kl} as follows. By a series of integrations by parts, the operator $[F, \cdot]$ is "turned" from the functions $u_l(x)$ to the function $\varrho(x)\, u_k(x)$. By the expression "turned" (instead of, for example, "displaced"), I wish to indicate that the *sequence* of the operations is thereby just reversed. The integrated parts occurring as "by-products" should disappear (see above). The "turned" operator, including the change in sign taking place when the number of differentiations is odd, is denoted by $[\bar{F}, \cdot\,]$. With the example (3):

$$[\bar{F}, \cdot] = (-1)^{\tau} \ldots K^2 \frac{\partial^2}{\partial q_{s''}\, \partial q_{r''}} h(q_1 \ldots q_n)\, K \frac{\partial}{\partial q_{r'}}$$

$$g(q_1 \ldots q_n)\, K^3 \frac{\partial^3}{\partial q_t\, \partial q_s\, \partial q_r} f(q_1 \ldots q_n). \qquad (3')$$

(τ = number of differentiations). Using this symbol, we obtain

$$F^{kl} = \int u_l(x)\, [\bar{F}, \varrho(x)\, u_k(x)]\, dx. \qquad (6')$$

If we now calculate the product matrix, we obtain

$$\sum_l F^{kl} G^{lm} = \sum_l \left\{ \int u_l(\varphi)\, [\bar{F}, \varrho(x)\, u_k(x)]\, dx \cdot \int \varrho(x)\, u_l(x) \cdot [G, u_m(x)]\, dx \right\}$$

$$= \int [\bar{F}, \varrho(x)\, u_k(x)]\, [G, u_m(x)]\, dx. \qquad (8)$$

The last equality is nothing other than the so-called "completeness relation" of our orthogonal system† applied to the "expansion coefficients" of the functions

$$[G, u_m(x)] \quad \text{and} \quad \frac{1}{\varrho(x)} [\bar{F}, \varrho(x)\, u_k(x)].$$

† See, for example, Courant-Hilbert, *Methoden der mathematischen Physik I*, p. 26, It is important to bear in mind that the completeness relation for the "expansion coefficient" holds for any case, even when the expansions themselves do *not* converge. If they converge, the equality (8) is immediately evident.

Now, in (8), by further integrations by parts, we turn the operator $[\bar{F}, \cdot]$ away from the function $\varrho(x)u_k(x)$ to the function $[G, u_m(x)]$, the operator acquiring its original form again. We obviously obtain:

$$(FG)^{km} = \sum_l F^{kl} G^{lm} = \int \varrho(x)\, u_k(x)\, [FG, u_m(x)]\, dx. \tag{9}$$

On the left is the km-th element of the product matrix and on the right, according to the assignment law (6) the km-th element of the matrix corresponding to the well-ordered product FG. Q.E.D.

§ 3. Heisenberg's Quantum Condition and the Rules for Partial Differentiation

Since the operation (1) is the identity, the well-ordered function

$$p_l q_l - q_l p_l \tag{10}$$

corresponds, according to our correlation law, in which, as will be remembered, we also included a universal constant K, to the operator: multiplication by K. Consequently, the *matrix*:

$$\begin{aligned}(p_l q_l - q_l p_l)^{ik} = K \int \varrho(x)\, u_i(x)\, u_k(x)\, dx &= 0 \quad \text{for} \quad i \neq k \\ &= K \quad \text{for} \quad i = k.\end{aligned} \tag{11}$$

This is Heisenberg's "quantum relation" if we put

$$K = \frac{h}{2\pi\sqrt{-1}}, \tag{12}$$

which may be retained from now on. Obviously, we could also have found the relation (11) by multiplying the matrices assigned to the function q_l and p_l

$$\begin{aligned} q_l^{ik} &= \int q_l \varrho(x)\, u_i(x)\, u_k(x)\, dx, \\ p_l^{ik} &= K \int \varrho(x)\, u_i(x) \frac{\partial u_k(x)}{\partial q_l}\, dx \end{aligned} \tag{13}$$

in a different sequence and subtracting the two results.

Let us now turn to the "rule for partial differentiation". To partially differentiate with respect to q_l a well-ordered function such as (2) will mean† to differentiate it *at each point* where q_l occurs in it, without changing the sequence of the factors, and to add all the results. Then it is easy to show that the following equation between operators applies

$$\left[\frac{\partial F}{\partial q_l}, \cdot\right] = \frac{1}{K}[p_l F - F p_l, \cdot] \tag{14}$$

The argument is as follows. Instead of actually differentiating with respect to q_l, I can make it more convenient for myself and simply write beforehand p_l, which on passing to the operators is in any case replaced by $K\dfrac{\partial}{\partial q_l}$. I need only first divide by K. Secondly, however, according to this, when the total operator is applied to any function u the operator $\partial/\partial q_l$ will not simply act on those parts of F that contain q_l (as it *should*) but *wrongly* also on the function u affected by the total operator. *I correct this error accurately* by subtracting the operation $[Fp_l, \cdot]$.

Let us now consider partial differentiation with respect to a p_l. Its significance for a well-ordered function like (2) is even somewhat simpler than for $\partial/\partial q_l$, since the p_k occur only as power products. We imagine every power of p_l as resolved into individual factors, e.g. $p_l p_l p_l$ instead of p_l^3, and can then say: in partial differentiation with respect to p_l each *individual* p_l occurring in F is to be *omitted* once (all the other p_l remaining); all the results so obtained must be added. What effect does this have on the operator (3)? "Each individual $K\dfrac{\partial}{\partial q_l}$ is to be omitted once and all the results so obtained are to be added."

† With all these definitions, of course, we follow Heisenberg exactly. From the strictly logical standpoint, the following proof is actually superfluous and we could write rules (14) and (15) directly, since they have been proved by Heisenberg and are based only on the rules of sums, products, and commutators (11) that we have demonstrated.

I assert that according to this argument the operator equation:

$$\left[\frac{\partial F}{\partial p_l}, \cdot\right] = \frac{1}{K}[Fq_l - q_lF, \cdot] \tag{15}$$

holds. In fact: I imagine the operator $[Fq_l, \cdot]$ formed and now attempt, in this operator, "to displace q_l through F from right to left", i.e. by successive commutations to arrive at the operator $[q_lF, \cdot]$. The displacement encounters an obstacle only when, in carrying it out, I meet a $\partial/\partial q_l$. I cannot simply interchange q_l with this, but inside the operator I must replace

$$\frac{\partial}{\partial q_l} \quad \text{by} \quad 1 + q_l \frac{\partial}{\partial q_l}. \tag{16}$$

As can easily be seen, the by-products of the commutation yielded by this "one-by-one" form just the desired "partial differential quotient". After the completion of the displacement, the operator $[q_lF, \cdot]$ remains; this would be superfluous and is therefore explicitly subtracted in (15). This therefore also proves (15). The Equations (14) and (15) proved for the *operators* naturally apply unchanged between the matrices belonging to the right-hand and left-hand sides since through (6) a linear operator belongs to one and only one matrix (with, of course, a previously selected system of functions $u_i(x)$).†

† It may be remarked incidentally that the converse of this statement applies, at least in the sense that with a given orthogonal system and density function certainly *not more than one* linear differential operator according to our correlation law (6) can belong to a given *matrix*. For, in (6) let the F^{kl} be given, let $[F, \cdot]$ be the linear operator *sought*, the *existence* of which we *assume*, and let $\varphi(x)$ be a partially continuous function of the $q_1, q_2 \dots q_n$ which must be differentiable sufficiently frequently but is otherwise quite arbitrary. Then the *completeness relation*, applied to the functions $\varphi(x)$ and $[F, u_k(x)]$ yield the following relation:

$$\int \varrho(x)\, \varphi(x)\, [F, u_k(x)]\, dx = \Sigma\left\{\int \varrho(x)\, \varphi(x)\, u_l(x)\, dx \cdot \int \varrho(x)\, u_l(x)\, [F, u_k(x)]\, dx\right\}.$$

The right-hand side can be regarded as known unambiguously; only the expansion coefficients of $\varphi(x)$ and the given matrix elements F^{lk} occur in it. By "turning" (see above) the left-hand side can be changed into the

§ 4. The Solution of Heisenberg's Equations of Motion

We have now shown that the matrices made from well-ordered functions by means of any complete orthogonal systems (4) by the definitions (3) and (6) satisfy all Heisenberg's rules of calculation, including the commutation rule (11). Now let us first consider a special mechanical problem characterized by a definite Hamiltonian function

$$H(q_k, p_k). \tag{17}$$

The authors of quantum mechanics take this function directly from *conventional* mechanics which, of course, does *not yield* it in "well-ordered" form, since in the conventional analysis there is no question of the sequence of factors. They then "normalize" or "symmetrize" the function in a certain manner for the purposes of quantum mechanics by, for example, replacing the conventional mechanical function $q_k p_k^2$ by

$$\tfrac{1}{2}(p_k^2 q_k + q_k p_k^2)$$

or by $p_k q_k p_k$, or by

$$\tfrac{1}{3}(p_k^2 q_k + p_k q_k p_k + q_k p_k^2),$$

---

k-th expansion coefficient of the function

$$\frac{[F, \varrho(x)\, \varphi(x)]}{\varrho(x)}.$$

Consequently, all the expansion coefficients of this function are unambiguously determined and therefore this function itself, also ("Courant–Hilbert", p. 37). Since, now, however, $\varrho(x)$ is fixed beforehand and $\varphi(x)$ is a completely arbitrary function, we can say: the result of the action of the *turned* operator on *any* function made only in such a way that it can be subjected to the action of the operator at all is determined *unambiguously* by the matrix F^{kl}. However, this means nothing but: the *turned operator* is determined unambiguously, since the concept "operator" is logically identical with the totality of the results of its action. From the turned operator, by turning, we obtain what is sought, unambiguously.

It should be borne in mind that the expansibility of the functions occurring need *not* be assumed. We have not proved that there is always a linear operator for any matrix.

which, according to (11), are all the same. This function must then be taken as "well-ordered", i.e. the sequence of factors has to be taken as untouchable. I will not go into the general symmetrization rule here;† the points of view are, if I understand correctly: H^{ki} is to be a *diagonal matrix*; otherwise the symmetrized function, regarded as a function of the conventional analysis, will be identical with that originally given.‡ We shall satisfy these requirements in a direct way.

Then the authors require that the *matrices* q_l^{ik}, p_l^{ik} shall satisfy an infinite system of equations as "equations of motion", which they originally write as follows:

$$\left.\begin{aligned} \left(\frac{dq_l}{dt}\right)^{ik} &= \left(\frac{\partial H}{\partial p_l}\right)^{ik} \\ \left(\frac{dp_l}{dt}\right)^{ik} &= \left(-\frac{\partial H}{\partial q_l}\right)^{ik} \end{aligned}\right\} \quad \begin{aligned} l &= 1, 2, 3 \ldots n \\ i, k &= 1, 2, 3 \ldots \end{aligned} \tag{18}$$

The upper pair of indices means, exactly as in the case of F^{ki}, above, the element concerned of the matrix belonging to the well-ordered function concerned. The significance of the partial differential quotients on the right-hand side has also been explained above, but *not* the d/dt occurring on the left-hand side. By this the authors mean: a series of *numbers*

$$\nu_1, \nu_2, \nu_3, \nu_4 \ldots \tag{19}$$

will be *given* such that the upper equation is satisfied when we give d/dt the meaning: multiplication of the ik-th matrix element by $2\pi\sqrt{-1}\,(\nu_i - \nu_k)$ Therefore, in particular

$$\begin{aligned} \left(\frac{dq_l}{dt}\right)^{ik} &= 2\pi\sqrt{-1}\,(\nu_i - \nu_k)\, q_l^{ik}; \\ \left(\frac{dp_l}{dt}\right)^{ik} &= 2\pi\sqrt{-1}\,(\nu_i - \nu_k)\, p_l^{ik}. \end{aligned} \tag{20}$$

† "Quantum mechanics I", pp. 873f.

‡ The *stronger* condition: shall give the same quantum-mechanical equations of motion, I consider to be too narrow. In my opinion it is based on the fact that the authors limit themselves to *power products even with respect to the* q_k, which is unnecessary.

The series of numbers (19) is, however, not necessarily determined beforehand but forms together with the matrix elements q_l^{ik}, p_l^{ik} the numerical unknowns of the system of equations (18). With the explanation of symbols (20), with the rules of calculation (14) and (15), and with (12) taken into consideration, this assumes the following form:

$$(\nu_i - \nu_k)\, q_l^{ik} = \frac{1}{h}(Hq_l - q_l H),$$

$$(\nu_i - \nu_k)\, p_l^{ik} = \frac{1}{h}(Hp_l - p_l H) \qquad (18')$$

(we have divided by $2\pi\sqrt{-1}$).

We also have to satisfy *this* system of equations and have no means available for this other than the suitable choice of the orthogonal system (4) upon which the matrix formation is based. I now state the following:

1. Equations (18′) are generally satisfied by choosing as orthogonal system the *eigenfunctions* of the natural eigenvalue problem of the following partial differential equation:

$$-[H, \psi] + E\psi = 0. \qquad (21)$$

ψ is an unknown function of $q_1, q_2 \cdots q_n$; E is the eigenvalue parameter. Obviously, both functions of $q_1 \cdots q_n$ occur as the density function $\varrho(x)$ by which Equation (21) must be multiplied in order to make it self-adjoint. The quantities ν_i are equal to the eigenvalues E_i divided by h. H^{kl} becomes a diagonal matrix with $H^{kk} = E_k$.

2. If the symmetrization of the function H has been carried out *in a suitable manner*—in my opinion the symmetrization process is not unambiguously defined beforehand—(21) is *identical with the wave equation upon which my wave mechanics is based.*†

Statements 1 are almost immediately evident if we provisionally first disregard the questions as to whether Equation (21) gives rise to a reasonable eigenvalue problem with as domain the

† *Ann. d. Phys.* **79**, p. 510, 1926 (Equation 18″). (This volume, p. 121.)

whole q-space at all, or whether it can always be made a self-adjoint one by multiplication by a suitable function, and so on. These questions are in fact settled to a large extent under 2.

Since, now, according to (21) and according to the definitions of the eigenvalues and eigenfunctions

$$[H, u_i] = E_i u_i, \tag{22}$$

according to (6)

$$\begin{aligned} H^{kl} &= \int \varrho(x)\, u_k(x)\, [H, u_l(x)]\, dx = E_l \int \varrho(x)\, u_k(x)\, u_l(x)\, dx \\ &= 0 \quad \text{for} \quad l \neq k \\ &= E_l \quad \text{for} \quad l = k \end{aligned} \tag{23}$$

and, for example,

$$\begin{aligned} (Hq_l)^{ik} &= \sum_m H^{im} q_l^{mk} = E_i q_l^{ik}, \\ (q_l H)^{ik} &= \sum_m q_l^{im} H^{mk} = E_k q_l^{ik}, \end{aligned} \tag{24}$$

so that the right-hand side of the first equation (18′) has the value:

$$\frac{E_i - E_k}{h} q_l^{ik}. \tag{25}$$

A completely similar argument holds for the second equation. Consequently, all statements under 1 have been proved.

We now turn to statement 2, i.e. agreement of the operator taken as negative of the (suitably symmetrized) Hamiltonian function with the wave operator of wave mechanics. I will first explain on the basis of a simple example why the symmetrization process does not seem to me *a priori* unambiguous. With *one* degree of freedom, let the *conventional* Hamiltonian function be

$$H = \tfrac{1}{2}(p^2 + q^2). \tag{26}$$

Then, obviously, in the first place this function can be taken over unchanged just as it stands as a "well-ordered" function into "quantum mechanics". However, we can also, and as in fact it appears to me *a priori* with the same justification, use the well-ordered function

$$H = \frac{1}{2}\left(\frac{1}{f(q)}pf(q)\,p + q^2\right) \tag{27}$$

where $f(q)$ is an arbitrary function within wide limits. In this case, $f(q)$ would occur as a "density function" $\varrho(x)$. (26) is quite obviously only a special case of (27) and the question arises as to whether and how it is possible at all to symbolize the special case that is intended generally, i.e. even for complicated H functions. It is still too inconvenient just in the most important application to restrict oneself at will even in the q_k to power products (where, of course, we could simply forbid the "production of denominators"). Moreover, as I believe, this does *not* lead to correct symmetrization.

For the convenience of the reader, I will now repeat the short derivation of the wave equation here in the form suitable for the present purposes. In this, I limit myself to the case of classical mechanics (without relativity or magnetic fields). Let therefore

$$H = T(q_k, p_k) + V(q_k) \tag{28}$$

and T be a quadratic form of the p_k. Then the wave equation can be obtained† from the following variational problem:

$$\delta J_1 = \delta \int \left\{\frac{h^2}{4\pi^2} T\left(q_k, \frac{\partial \psi}{\partial q_k}\right) + \psi^2 V(q_k)\right\} \Delta_p^{-\frac{1}{2}}\, dx = 0 \tag{29}$$

with the auxiliary condition

$$J_2 = \int \psi^2 \Delta_p^{-\frac{1}{2}}\, dx = 1.$$

$\int dx$ stands, as above, for $\int \cdots \int dq_1 \cdots dq_n$; $\Delta_p^{-\frac{1}{2}}$ is the *reciprocal square root of the discriminant* of the quadratic form T. *This factor must by no means be left out,* since otherwise the whole process would not be invariant with respect to point transformations of the q_k. On the other hand, however, another

† *Ann. d. Phys.* **79**, p. 376, 1926. Equations (23) and (24).

explicit function of the q_k could come in as factor, i.e. a function which is invariant under a point transformation of the q_k. (It is known that this does not apply to Δ_p, otherwise it *would* in fact be possible to omit $\Delta_p^{-\frac{1}{2}}$ by giving to this extra function the value $\Delta_p^{\frac{1}{2}}$.)

If we indicate by the index p_k the derivation of T by the particular argument that originally read p_k, we obtain as the *result of the variation*:

$$0 = \frac{1}{2}(\delta J_1 - E\delta J_2)$$

$$= \int \left\{ -\frac{h^2}{8\pi^2} \sum_k \frac{\partial}{\partial q_k} \left(\Delta_p^{-\frac{1}{2}} T_{p_k} \left(q_k, \frac{\partial \psi}{\partial q_k} \right) \right) + (V(q_k) - E) \Delta_p^{-\frac{1}{2}} \psi \right\}$$
$$\times\ \delta\psi\, dx; \tag{30}$$

Euler's variational equation therefore is:

$$\frac{h^2}{8\pi^2} \Delta_p^{\frac{1}{2}} \sum_k \frac{\partial}{\partial q_k} \left\{ \Delta_p^{-\frac{1}{2}} T_{p_k} \left(q_k, \frac{\partial \psi}{\partial q_k} \right) \right\} - V(q_k)\, \psi + E\psi = 0. \tag{31}$$

It is easy to see that the equation has the form (21) if we recall our law of operator correlation and take into account the Euler relation for homogeneous functions, applied to the quadratic form T:

$$T(q_k, p_k) = \tfrac{1}{2} \sum_k p_k T_{p_k}(q_k, p_k). \tag{32}$$

In actual fact: if the operator is detached from the left-hand side of (31), with the exception of the eigenvalue term $E\psi$, and

$$\frac{h}{2\pi \sqrt{-1}} \frac{\partial}{\partial q_k}$$

in it is replaced by p_k, according to (32) we obtain the negative Hamiltonian function (28). In this argument, the variational process has quite automatically given an unambiguously determined "symmetrization" of the operator which makes it self-adjoint, except for a factor, and invariant to point transformations and to which I should like to adhere as long as no completely definite reasons are in favour of the additional factor under the integrals

(29) that was mentioned as possible above† and of a definite form of it.

Consequently, therefore, the resolution of the whole system of the Heisenberg–Born–Jordan matrix equations is brought back to the natural eigenvalue problem of a linear partial differential equation. When the eigenvalue problem has been solved, each matrix element in which we are interested can be calculated according to the instruction (6) by differentiations and quadratures.

To explain what is to be understood here by the *natural* eigenvalue problem, i.e. by the natural boundary conditions at the natural boundary of the configuration space, I refer to the calculated examples.‡ It appears regularly that the natural infinitely distant boundary forms a singularity of the differential equation and unambiguously permits only the one boundary condition: "remain finite". This might be a common characteristic feature of the micromechanical problems primarily coming into consideration for the application of the theory. If the range of position coordinates is artificially limited (example: molecule in a "box"), we shall have to take account of this limitation fundamentally in the well-known manner by introducing suitable potential energies. The *disappearance* of the eigenfunctions at the boundary is also satisfied in general to a very far-reaching extent even if with *certain* of the integrals (6) situations exist which make a special consideration necessary and into which I cannot go at the moment (this relates to those matrix elements in the Kepler problem which, according to Heisenberg, correspond to the transition from hyperbolic path to hyperbolic path).

I have limited myself here to the case of classical mechanics without a magnetic field, since the relativistic-magnetic generalization does not yet appear to me to be sufficiently elucidated. However, that the complete parallelism of the two new quantum theories will remain valid for this as well can hardly be doubted.

Finally, another general observation on the whole apparatus of §§ 2, 3 and 4. In all formulae, the orthogonal system used as

† See also *Ann. d. Phys.* **79**, p. 362, and p. 510, 1926.

‡ See the papers cited above (this volume, pp. 94 and 106).

a basis has been regarded as a *discrete* system of functions. In the most important applications this is precisely *not* the case. Not only in the case of the hydrogen atom, but also with other atoms the wave equation (31) must possess not only a line spectrum but also a continuous eigenvalue spectrum which shows itself, *inter alia*, in the continuous *optical* spectra that border on the series limit. It appeared better provisionally not to load the formulae and arguments with this, in fact indispensable, generalizaton. The main purpose of this note is actually to work out the formal relationships of the two theories as clearly as possible and this will certainly not be changed essentially by the occurrence of a continuous spectrum. An important caution: we have never assumed, without further information, the convergence of the expansion in terms of the eigenfunctions. This caution is imposed quite particularly by the *accumulation of the discrete eigenvalues at a finite value* (at the series limit), which, for its part, is extremely closely connected with the occurrence of the continuous spectrum.

§ 5. Comparison of the Two Theories. Glimpse at a Classical Relationship of the Intensity and Polarization of the Emitted Radiation

If the two theories—I could properly also use the singular—should prove tenable in the form in which they are currently stated, i.e. already as the correct generalization for even complicated systems,† any discussion of the advantage of one or the

† There is a special reason for considering this to be questionable. Provisionally, both theories take over the energy function from classical mechanics. Now the *potential* energy in the cases so far treated consists in the interaction of mass points of which perhaps at least *one*, because of its large mass, can be regarded as point-shaped even from the point of view of wave mechanics (cf. A. Einstein, *Berl. Ber.*, 1925, p. 10). The possibility must be reckoned with that the taking over of the formula for the potential anergy from classical mechanics is no longer permissible when *both* "point charges" are actually extended states of vibration which penetrate into one another.

other has, in a certain sense, only an apparent value. For from the purely mathematical point of view, they are in fact completely equivalent and it can only be a question of the basically subordinate question of convenience of calculation.

Today there are not a few physicists who, completely in the spirit of Kirchhoff and Mach, regard the task of physical theory as merely an as *economical as possible* mathematical description of the empirical relationships between observable quantities, i.e. a description which represents the relationship as far as possible without the intermediary of elements unobservable in principle. With such an attitude, mathematical equivalence means almost the same as physical equivalence. At the most, in the present case, a certain advantage of the matrix representation could be seen in the fact that, because of its complete lack of visualizability, it does not mislead us into forming space-time pictures of the atomistic phenomenon which must perhaps remain uncontrollable in principle. In this respect, however, the following *supplementation* of the proof of equivalents given above is of interest in any case: the equivalence *actually* exists and it also exists *in the opposite direction.* Not only can the matrices be constructed from the eigenfunctions, as shown above, but, conversely, the eigenfunctions can also be constructed from the numerically given matrices. Consequently, the latter do not form something like an *arbitrary* and *special* "incarnation" of the bare matrix skeleton pandering to the desire for visualizability, which would in fact justify an intuitive and theoretical preference for the latter. In the equations

$$q_l^{ik} = \int u_i(x)\, q_l u_k(x)\, dx \tag{33}$$

let us consider the *left-hand* sides as given numerically and the functions $u_i(x)$ sought. (NB: the "density function" is purposely omitted, and the $u_i(x)$ will *themselves* for the moment be orthogonal functions.) Then the integrals

$$\int P(x)\, u_i(x)\, u_k(x)\, dx \tag{34}$$

in which $P(x)$ is *any* power product of the q_l, can be calculated by matrix multiplication, in which, moreover, no "turning", i.e. integration by parts, is necessary. The totality of these integrals, with a fixed i and k, forms what is called the totality of the "*moments*" of the function $u_i(x)$, and it is known that under very general conditions a function is determined unambiguously by the totality of its moments. Consequently, all the products $u_i(x)u_k(x)$ are determined unambiguously, including the squares $u_i(x)^2$, and therefore also the $u_i(x)$ themselves. The only arbitrariness lies in the subsequent resolution of the density function $\varrho(x)$, e.g. $r^2 \sin\vartheta$ in the case of polar spatial coordinates. Here, in any case, we need not fear any *intuitive-theoretical* faux pas.

In addition, however, this thesis that mathematical equivalence is the same thing as physical equivalence, can be assigned only limited validity. We may think, for example, of the two expressions for the electrostatic energy of a system of charged conductors, as a space integral $\frac{1}{2}\int \boldsymbol{E}^2 d\tau$ and as the sum over the conductors $\frac{1}{2}\sum e_i V_i$. The two expressions are completely equivalent for electrostatics, and one can be obtained from the other via an ingegration by parts. Nevertheless, we greatly prefer the former and say that *it* correctly localizes the energy in space. This preference can obviously never be based on the foundation of electrostatics but only because the first expression remains useful in electrodynamics as well, while the second does not.

Which of the two new quantum theories deserves preference from *this* point of view can hardly be decided with certainty today. As the natural representative of one of them, however, I shall not be blamed if I unreservedly—and perhaps without being able to avoid a certain one-sidedness—stress the arguments in its favour.

The problems, apart from the inherently optical questions, that come into consideration for the further development of atom dynamics are shown us by experimental physics in an eminently clear form such as, for example: how do two colliding atoms or molecules recoil from one another; how is an electron or an α-particle deflected when it is projected with a certain velocity and areal velocity ("perpendicular from the nucleus to the initial orbit") through an atom? To treat such problems in more detail, it is absolutely necessary to review clearly the continuous transition between the macroscopic visible mechanics and the micromechanics of the atom. I have recently† explained how I regard this transition. Micromechanics represents a refinement of macromechanics which is made necessary by the geometrical and mechanical smallness of the objects and is of just the same kind as the transition from geometrical to physical optics; the latter holds sway as soon as the wavelength is no longer very large as compared with the dimensions of the objects under investigation or compared with those spatial measurements within which it is desired to obtain accurate information on the distribution of light.

It appears to me to be extraordinarily difficult to attack problems of the type sketched above as long as, on the basis of a theory of knowledge, we consider ourselves bound in atom dynamics to suppress intuition and to operate only with abstract concepts such as transition probabilities, energy levels, and the like.

A particularly important question which is perhaps the cardinal question of the whole of atom dynamics is, as is well known, the question of the *coupling* between the atomic-dynamic phenomenon and the electromagnetic field or what has perhaps to come in place of the latter. Not only does the whole complex of questions of dispersion, resonance and secondary radiation, and natural line width belong here, but the designation of certain atomic-dynamic quantities such as emission frequencies, line intensities, . . ., acquires a more than dogmatic significance only when the coupling is described mathematically in some form or other. Here the matrix representation of atom dynamics has now led to the assumption that in fact the electromagnetic field, also, *must* be represented differently—namely by the matrix method—in order to be able to formulate the coupling mathematically. Wave mechanics shows that there is in any case no compulsion about this, since the mechanical field scalar (which I denote

† *Ann. d. Phys.* **79**, p. 484, 1926.

by ψ) is actually completely suitable for insertion in the unchanged Maxwell–Lorentz equations between the electromagnetic field vectors, as the "source" of them; just as, conversely, the electrodynamic potentials come in the coefficients of the wave equation that determines the mechanical field scalar.† In any case, it is worthwhile just to *seek* the representation of the coupling in such a way that a four-vector derived in a suitable manner from the mechanical field scalar ψ of the movement of the electrons (perhaps by means of the field vectors themselves or the potentials) is inserted in the unchanged Maxwell–Lorentz equations as the *four-current*. In fact there is some hope that the wave equation for ψ could also be represented as a consequence of the Maxwell–Lorentz equations, namely as a continuity equation of the electricity.

The difficulty which occurs for the *multi*-electron problem in that ψ is actually a function in *configuration* space and not in actual space must not remain unmentioned. Nevertheless, with respect to the one-electron problem I should like to explain in somewhat more detail that it might be possible in this way to give an extraordinarily graphical explanation of the intensity and polarization of the radiation.

Let us consider the wave-mechanical picture of the hydrogen atom in a state where the mechanical field scalar ψ is given by a series of discrete eigenfunctions:

$$\psi = \sum_k c_k u_k(x)\, e^{(2\pi\sqrt{-1}\,E_k)t/h} \tag{35}$$

† Similar thoughts have been expressed by K. Lanczos in an interesting note that has recently appeared (*Ztschr. f. Phys.* **35**, p. 812, 1926), which likewise contains the valuable result that Heisenberg's atom dynamics is also capable of a continuous interpretation. Otherwise, however, Lanczos' paper has fewer direct points of contact with the present paper than would be thought at first sight. The determinaton of Lanczos' system of formulae, provisionally left quite indefinite, is *not* to be sought in the direction that Lanczos' symmetrical kernel $K(s, \sigma)$ is to be identified with the *Green function* of our wave equation (21) or (31), since this Green function, if it exists, has the quantum levels themselves for eigenvalues. In contrast, it is required of Lanczos' kernel that it should have the *reciprocal* quantum levels as eigenvalues.

(here x stands for *three* variables, such as r, ϑ, and φ; we consider the c_k to be real, and on the right the real part is to be taken). We now make the *assumption* that the space density of the electricity is given by the real part of

$$\psi \frac{\partial \bar{\psi}}{\partial t}. \tag{36}$$

Here the bar denotes the conjugate complex. Then we calculate for the space density

$$\text{Space density} = 2\pi \sum_{(k,m)} c_k c_m \frac{E_k - E_m}{h} u_k(x)\, u_m(x) \times \sin \frac{2\pi t}{h}(E_m - E_k), \tag{37}$$

where the sum is to be extended over each combination (k, m) only once. Now only the term *differences* still occur as frequencies in (37). These are so small that the corresponding wavelength in the ether is large as compared with the dimensions of the atom, i.e. as compared with that range within which (37) is appreciably different from zero at all.† The emitted radiation can therefore be evaluated simply from the *dipole moment* that the whole atom possesses according to (37). We multiply (37) by a Cartesian coordinate q_l and by the "density function" $\varrho(x)$ (in the present case, $r^2 \sin \vartheta$) and integrate over the whole of space. According to (13), we obtain for the component of the dipole moment in the direction q_l

$$Mq_l = 2\pi \sum_{(k,m)} c_k c_m q_l^{km} \frac{E_k - E_m}{h} \sin \frac{2\pi t}{h}(E_m - E_k). \tag{38}$$

We thus obtain, in fact, a "Fourier expansion" of the electric moment of the atom in which only the term *differences* occur as frequencies. The coefficients contain Heisenberg's matrix elements q_l^{km} in such a way that their determining influence on the intensity and polarization of the corresponding part of the emitted radiation becomes completely understandable on the basis of classical electrodynamics.

† *Ann. d. Phys.* **79**, p. 371, 1926 (this volume, p. 105).

The above sketch of the mechanism of the radiation is still far from completely satisfactory and by no means definitive. The formula (36) makes use of a complex apparatus of calculation in a somewhat free manner to eliminate undesirable components of the vibration the radiation of which can by no means be investigated in the simple manner using the dipole moment of the whole atom, since the corresponding wavelengths in the ether (about 0·01 Å) are far below the dimensions of the atom. Moreover, the space density (37), when the integration is carried out over the whole of space, gives zero according to (5) and not, as must be required, a finite value, independent of the time, which must be normalized to the electronic charge. Finally, to complete the picture, the magnetic radiation would have to be taken into account, since with a spatial distribution of the flow of electricity radiation is possible even without an electric moment appearing at all, e.g. with a loop antenna.

Nevertheless, the hope that a true understanding of the state of the emitted radiation can be obtained on the basis of an analytical mechanism very similar to that sketched here appears to be well justified.

PAPER 5

Quantization as an Eigenvalue Problem†

E. SCHRÖDINGER

(4th Communication‡)

§ 1. Elimination of the Energy Parameter from the Oscillation Equation. The True Wave Equation. Non-Conservative Systems

The wave equation (18) or (18″) of p. 121 of the second communication

$$\nabla^2\psi - \frac{2(E-V)}{E^2}\frac{\partial^2\psi}{\partial t^2} = 0 \tag{1}$$

or

$$\nabla^2\psi + \frac{8\pi^2}{h^2}(E-V)\psi = 0, \tag{1'}$$

which forms the *foundation* of the new basis of mechanics investigated in this series of papers, suffers from the defect that it does not give the law of change for the "mechanical field scalar" ψ *uniformly* and *generally*. Equation (1), in fact, contains the energy or frequency parameter E and is, as expressly stressed elsewhere, with a *definite* value of E valid for processes which depend on the *time* exclusively through a definite periodic factor

$$\psi \sim P \cdot R \cdot (e^{\pm(2\pi i Et)/h}). \tag{2}$$

† *Annalen der Physik*, **81**, 109, 1926.

‡ Cf. *Ann. d. Phys.* **79**, p. 361, 489 (see this volume, pp. 94 and 106); **80**, p. 437, 1926; also, on the relationship with Heisenbergs's theory, *ibid.* **79**, p. 734 (this volume, p. 127).

Equation (1) is therefore in reality no more general than Equation (1′), which takes account of the circumstance just mentioned and, in fact, no longer contains the time.

If, therefore, we have occasionally called Equation (1) or (1′) a "wave equation", this was actually incorrect; it would be more correct to call it a "vibration" or "amplitude" equation. However, we found this adequate, since it is just to *this* that the Sturm–Liouville eigenvalue problem is linked—just as with the mathematically completely analogous problem of the free vibrations of strings and membranes, and not the *true* wave equation.

In these circumstances, we have previously always assumed that the potential energy V is a pure coordinate function and does *not* depend explicitly on the time. However, the pressing need exists to extend the theory to non-conservative systems, since only in this way can the behaviour of the system under the action of predetermined external forces—e.g., a light wave or a passing foreign atom—be studied. However, as soon as V contains the time explicitly, it is obviously *impossible* to satisfy Equation (1) or (1′) by means of a function ψ which depends on the time only in accordance with (2). Consequently, the amplitude equation is no longer adequate, but the true wave equation must be used. This can easily be given for conservative systems. In this case, (2) is equivalent to

$$\frac{\partial^2 \psi}{\partial t^2} = -\frac{4\pi^2 E^2}{h^2}\psi. \tag{3}$$

E can be eliminated by differentiations from (1′) and (3) and we obtain in an easily understandable symbolic method of writing

$$\left(\nabla^2 - \frac{8\pi^2}{h^2}V\right)^2 \psi + \frac{16\pi^2}{h^2}\frac{\partial^2 \psi}{\partial t^2} = 0. \tag{4}$$

This equation has to satisfy every ψ which, according to (2), but *with any E*, depends on the time; consequently also every ψ that can be expanded in a Fourier series with respect to the time (with coordinate functions as coefficients, of course). Equation (4) is therefore obviously the *uniform and general wave equation for the field scalar* ψ.

As can be seen, it is no longer of the very simple type of the vibrating membrane but is, rather, in coordinates of the *fourth* order and of a very similar type to that which occurs in many problems of elasticity theory.† However, no excessive complication of the theory due to this is to be feared nor, indeed, the necessity of a revision of the methods given previously and connected with Equation (1′). If V does *not* contain the time, we can, starting from (4), produce the formula (2) and then resolve the operator in (4) in the following way:

$$\left(\nabla^2 - \frac{8\pi^2}{h^2}V + \frac{8\pi^2}{h^2}E\right)\left(\nabla^2 - \frac{8\pi^2}{h^2}V - \frac{8\pi^2}{h^2}E\right)\psi = 0. \quad (4')$$

This equation can be resolved *experimentally* into two equations linked by "either—or", namely into Equation (1′) and another which differs from (1′) only by the fact that in it the eigenvalue parameter *is called* minus E instead of plus E, which according to (2) does not lead to new solutions. The resolution of (4′) is not obligatory, since the law that "a product can only disappear when at least *one* factor disappears" does not apply to operators. This lack of necessity, however, is associated with the methods for the step-by-step solution of partial differential equations. The process is justified subsequently by the proof of the completeness of the eigenfunctions found as functions of the coordinate. In combination with the fact that not only the real part but also the imaginary part of (2) satisfies Equation (4), it permits any desired initial conditions for ψ and $\partial\psi/\partial t$ to be satisfied.

We therefore see that the wavee quation (4), which includes the dispersion law within it, can in fact act as a basis of the theory of conservative systems previously developed. Its generalization for

† E.g. for a vibrating *plate*: $\nabla^2\nabla^2 u + \frac{\partial^2 u}{\partial t^2} = 0$. Cf. Courant-Hilbert, Chapter V, § 8, p. 256.

the case of a time-variable potential function, however, requires some caution, since in this process terms with time derivatives of V may occur concerning which Equation (4), because of the nature of its derivation, can naturally give us no information. In fact, in the attempt to apply Equation (4) as it stands to non-conservative systems we come up against complications which appear to arise from a term with $\partial V/\partial t$. Consequently, below I have followed a somewhat different path which is simpler to an extraordinary degree from the point of view of calculation and which I regard as correct in principle.

The order of the wave equation *need* not be brought down to four in order to remove the energy parameter from it. The time dependence of ψ necessary for the validity of (1′) can be expressed not only by (3) but also by

$$\frac{\partial \psi}{\partial t} = \pm \frac{2\pi i}{h} E\psi. \tag{3'}$$

We then come to one of the two equations

$$\nabla^2\psi - \frac{8\pi^2}{h^2} V\psi \mp \frac{4\pi i}{h} \frac{\partial \psi}{\partial t} = 0. \tag{4''}$$

We shall require that the complex wave function ψ satisfied one of these two equations. Since then the conjugate complex function $\bar{\psi}$ satisfies the *other* equation, it will be possible to regard the real part of ψ as a real wave function (when it is required). In the case of a conservative system, (4″) is substantially equivalent to (4), since, when V does not contain the time, the real operator can be resolved into the product of the two conjugate complex ones.

§ 2. Extension of the Perturbation Theory to Perturbations explicitly containing the Time. Dispersion Theory

The main interest is not directed to systems in which the temporal variations of the potential energy V are of the same order of magnitude as the spatial variations, but to systems which, in themselves conservative, are *perturbed* by the appearance of small given functions of the time (and of the coordinates) in the potential energy. We therefore assume

$$V = V_0(x) + r(x, t), \tag{5}$$

where x, as frequently before, stands as a representative of the totality of the configuration coordinates. The unperturbed eigenvalue problem ($r = 0$) we regard as *solved*. Then the perturbation problem can be solved by *quadratures*.

However, we do not want to treat the general problem immediately but to pick out of the large number of important applications falling under the above question the problem of *dispersion theory*, because of its outstanding importance which in any case thoroughly justifies a separate treatment. Here the perturbing forces arise from a uniform and harmonically vibrating electric field in the region of the atom and we therefore have to write for the perturbing potential, when it is a case of a linearly polarized monochromatic light of frequency ν, the equation:

$$r(x, t) = A(x) \cos 2\pi\nu t \tag{6}$$

therefore

$$V = V_0(x) + A(x) \cos 2\pi\nu t. \tag{5'}$$

Here, $A(x)$ is the negative product of the amplitude of the light and that coordinate function which, *according* to *classical mechanics*, denotes the component of the electric moment of the atom in the direction of the electric light vector (for example $-F\sum e_i z_i$, if F is the amplitude of the light, e_i and z_i are the charges and z-coordinates of the mass points, and the light is polarized in the z-direction (we borrow the part of the potential function *variable* with time from classical mechanics with just as much or just as little justification as we did the *constant* part earlier, e.g. in the Kepler problem).

With Relaton (5'), Equation (4'') becomes:

$$\nabla^2\psi - \frac{8\pi^2}{h^2}(V_0 + A \cos 2\pi\nu t)\,\psi \mp \frac{4\pi i}{h}\frac{\partial\psi}{\partial t} = 0. \tag{7}$$

For $A = 0$, these equations change via the relation:

$$\psi = u(x)\, c^{\pm(2\pi i Et)/h} \tag{8}$$

(which now is meant *not* as the "real part" but in the true sense) into the amplitude equation (1′) of the unperturbed problem, and it is known (cf. § 1) that the totality of the solutions of the unperturbed problem is found in this way. Let

$$E_k \text{ and } u_k(x), \quad k = 1, 2, 3 \ldots$$

be the eigenvalues and normalized eigenfunctions of the unperturbed problem, which we regard as *known* and which, in order that we shall lose nothing in the way of auxiliary questions, which will have to be considered specially, we shall assume to be *discrete* and *different* from one another (non-degenerate system without continuous spectrum).

We shall then have to seek solutions of the perturbed problem, exactly as in the case of a perturbing potential independent of the time, in the neighbourhood of *every* possible solution of the unperturbed problem, i.e. in the neighbourhood of any linear combination whatever with constant coefficients of the $u_k(x)$ [according to (8) to be associated with the appropriate time factors $e^{\pm(2\pi i E_k t)/h}$]. Physically, the solution of the perturbed problem located in the neighbourhood of a *definite* linear combination will have the significance that it is *this* which first comes into being when it is just this definite linear combination of free eigenvibrations that is present when the light wave arrives (possibly with slight changes in the "switching-on" process).

Since now, however, the equation of the perturbed problem is also *homogeneous*—this defect may be expressly stressed by analogy with "forced vibrations" in acoustics—it is obviously sufficient to seek the perturbed solution in the neighbourhood of each *individual*

$$u_k(x)\, e^{\pm(2\pi i E_k t)/h} \tag{9}$$

which can then be combined linearly ad libitum just as in the case of the unperturbed solutions.

Consequently, to solve the first equation (7) we assume the relation:

$$\psi = u_k(x)\, e^{(2\pi i E_k t)/h} + w(x, t). \tag{10}$$

[The lower sign, i.e. the second Equation (7), we can subsequently put aside; it would yield nothing new.] The additional term $w(x, t)$ may be regarded as small and its product with the perturbing potential can be neglected. If we take this into account in the substitution of (10) in (7) and bear in mind that $u_k(x)$ and E_k are the eigenfunction and eigenvalue of the unperturbed problem, we obtain:

$$\nabla^2 w - \frac{8\pi^2}{h^2} V_0 w - \frac{4\pi i}{h}\frac{\partial w}{\partial t} = \frac{8\pi^2}{h^2} A \cos 2\pi\nu t \cdot u_k e^{(2\pi i E_k t)/h}$$

$$= \frac{4\pi^2}{h^2} A u_k \cdot \left(e^{\frac{2\pi i t}{h}(E_k + h\nu)} + e^{\frac{2\pi i t}{h}(E_k - h\nu)}\right). \tag{11}$$

This equation can be satisfied easily and essentially *only* by the relation:

$$w = w_+(x)\, e^{\frac{2\pi i t}{h}(E_k + h\nu)} + w_-(x)\, e^{\frac{2\pi i t}{h}(E_k - h\nu)}, \tag{12}$$

if the two functions $w_\pm$ satisfy, respectively, the two equations

$$\nabla^2 w_\pm + \frac{8\pi^2}{h^2}(E_k \pm h\nu - V_0)\, w_\pm = \frac{4\pi^2}{h^2} A u_k. \tag{13}$$

This step is essentially *unambiguous*. In fact, it immediately appears that it is still possible to add to (12) any desired combination of unperturbed eigenvibrations. Only this combination must be assumed to be of the first order of smallness (since this assumption is made about w) and then offers no interest for the moment, since it causes perturbances of the second order at the most.

Now, finally, in Equations (13) we have those *inhomogeneous* equations in front of us that we might reasonably expect to encounter—in spite of the lack of analogy with true forced vibrations stressed above. This lack of analogy is extraordinarily important and shows itself in Equations (13) in the following two circumstances. *In the first place*, it is not the perturbing function $A(x)$ *alone* that appears as "second term" ("exciting force") but its *product* with the free amplitude of vibration already present. This is impermissible for the purpose of doing justice to the physical facts, since the reaction of the atoms to an incident light wave depends eminently on the *state* in which the atom actually exists, while the forced vibrations of a membrane, plate, ..., are, as is well known, quite independent of the eigenvibrations that may be superposed and would therefore give a completely unusable picture. *In the second place*, it is not the frequency ν of the perturbing force *alone* that appears on the left-hand side of (13) in place of the eigenvalue, i.e. as "exciting frequency", but rather in the one case its sum and in the other case its difference with respect to the free vibration already present. This is again an impermissible requirement, since otherwise eigenfrequencies themselves, which actually correspond to the *term* frequencies, would function as *resonance positions* and not, as is to be required and as Equation (13) actually gives, the *differences* of the eigenfrequencies, and, in fact, as we recognize with satisfaction: *only* the differences of an eigenfrequency that is *actually excited* with respect to all the others, and *not* the differences of pairs of eigenfrequencies of which *none* is excited.

In order to get a more accurate idea of this, let us carry the solution process to the end. By well-known methods,† we find as *unambiguous* solutions of (13):

$$w_{\pm}(x) = \frac{1}{2} \sum_{n=1}^{\infty} \frac{a'_{kn} u_n(x)}{E_k - E_n \pm h\nu} \tag{14}$$

with

$$a'_{kn} = \int A(x)\, u_k(x)\, u_n(x)\, \varrho(x)\, dx. \tag{15}$$

$\varrho(x)$ is the "density function", i.e. that function of the position coordinates by which Equation (1′) must be multiplied in order to make it a self-adjoint one. The $u_n(x)$ are assumed to be normalized. In addition, it is presumed that $h\nu$ *accurately agrees*

† Cf. 3rd communication, §§ 1 and 2, text to Equations (8) and (24).

with none of the eigenvalue differences $E_k - E_n$. We shall discuss this "resonance case" later (cf. § 4).

If, now, from (14) in accordance with (12) and (10), we construct the whole perturbed vibration, we obtain:

$$\psi = u_k(x)\, e^{(2\pi i E_k t)/h} + \frac{1}{2}\sum_{n=1}^{\infty} a'_{kn} u_n(x) \left(\frac{e^{\frac{2\pi i t}{h}(E_k + h\nu)}}{E_k - E_n + h\nu} + \frac{e^{\frac{2\pi i t}{h}(E_k - h\nu)}}{E_k - E_n - h\nu} \right). \tag{16}$$

Thus, in the case of perturbance with every *free* vibration $u_k(x)$ all those vibrations for which $a'_{kn} \neq 0$ also vibrate with a small amplitude. These are just those which, when they are compatible with u_k as free vibrations, give rise to radiation which is polarized (wholly or partially) in the direction of polarization of the incident wave, since a'_{kn} is, apart from a factor, nothing other than the amplitude component falling in this direction of polarization of the electric moment of the atom oscillating with the frequency $(E_k - E_n)/h$ *according to wave mechanics*, which occurs when u_k and u_n are compatible.†

However, the associated vibration takes place not with the proper eigenfrequency of these vibrations E_n/h and not with the frequency ν of the light wave, but rather with the sum and with the difference of E_k/h (i.e. the frequency of the *one* existing *free* vibration) and ν.

In order to determine the significance of our result for dispersion theory, we have to investigate the radiation that arises from the coexistence of the excited forced vibrations with the original free vibration already present. For this purpose, using the process always used hitherto‡—a critical discussion follows in § 7—we form the product of the complex wave function (16)

† See below and § 7.

‡ Cf. *Ann. d. Phys.* **79**, p. 755, 1926, and also the calculation of the intensities of the Stark effect in the 3rd communication. At the point first mentioned, instead of $\psi\bar{\psi}$ the real part of $\psi\dot{\psi}$ was proposed. This was an error, which was corrected in the 3rd communication.

and the conjugate complex value, i.e. the norm of the complex wave function ψ. In this, we take into account the fact that the perturbing members are small so that their squares and mutual products can be neglected. After easy reduction,† we obtain:

$$\psi\bar{\psi} = u_k(x)^2 + 2\cos 2\pi\nu t \sum_{n=1}^{\infty} \frac{(E_k - E_n)\, a'_{kn} u_k(x)\, u_n(x)}{(E_k - E_n)^2 - h\nu}. \tag{17}$$

According to the *heuristic hypothesis* concerning the electrodynamic interpretation of the field scalar ψ, which in the case of the Stark effect of hydrogen led us to the correct selection and polarization rules and to a very satisfactory representation of the intensity ratios, the above quantities—apart from a multiplicative constant—represent the density of the electricity as a function of the space coordinate and the time, *if x represents only three space coordinates*, i.e. if we are dealing with the *one*-electron problem. In a suitable generalization of this hypothesis —further details of which are given in § 7—we now, in the general case, regard as the density of the electricity that is "associated" with *one* of the mass points of classical mechanics or "is based upon it" or "corresponds wave-mechanically to it" the following: the *integral* of $\psi\bar{\psi}$ over all those system coordinates which in classical mechanics determine the position of the *other* mass points multiplied by a certain constant, the classical "charge" of the mass point considered. The total charge density in a space point is then represented by the sum of the integrals mentioned over all the mass points.

In order then to find any space component of the total wave-mechanical *dipole moment* as a function of the time, according to this hypothesis we must multiply the Expression (17) with that coordinate function which, in *classical mechanics*, gives the corresponding dipole component as a function of the configura-

† For the sake of simplicity, we assume as we always have done previously that the eigenfunctions $u_n(x)$ are *real*, but observe that under certain circumstances it is in fact very much more convenient to work with complex combinations of the real eigenfunctions, e.g. in the case of the eigenfunctions of the Kepler problem with $e^{+m\varphi i}$ instead of with $\genfrac{}{}{0pt}{}{\cos}{\sin}\, m\varphi$.

tion of the point system, i.e., for example, by

$$M_y = \sum e_i y_i, \tag{18}$$

when we are dealing with the dipole moment in the y-direction. Then we must integrate over *all* the configuration coordinates.

Let us carry this out. For brevity, let us put

$$b_{kn} = \int M_y(x)\, u_k(x)\, u_n(x)\, \varrho(x)\, dx. \tag{19}$$

Let us, moreover, elucidate the definition of the a'_{kn} according to (15), by recalling that, if the incident electric vector of the light is given by

$$E_z = F\cos 2\pi\nu t, \tag{20}$$

$A(x)$ has the significance

$$A(x) = -F\cdot M_z(x), \tag{21}$$

in which $M_z(x) = \sum e_i z_i$. If we then put, analogously to (19),

$$a_{kn} = \int M_z(x)\, u_k(x)\, u_n(x)\, \varrho(x)\, dx, \tag{22}$$

$a'_{kn} = -Fa_{kn}$ and by carrying out the projected integration, we find:

$$\int M_y \psi\bar{\psi}\varrho\, dx = a_{kk} + 2F\cos 2\pi\nu t \sum_{n=1}^{\infty} \frac{(E_n - E_k)a_{kn}b_{kn}}{(E_k - E_n)^2 - h^2\nu^2} \tag{23}$$

for *the resulting electric moment to which the secondary radiation is to be ascribed*, and which is produced by the incident wave (20).

For the emitted radiation, of course, only the second time-variable part is important, while the first represents the time-constant dipole moment which may be associated with the free vibrations existing originally. The variable part appears fairly reasonable and might correspond to all requirements that are customarily set for a "dispersion formula". We note, in particular, the occurrence of even those so-called "negative" terms which—in the usual terminology—correspond to the transition possibility to a lower level ($E_n < E_k$) and to which Kramers first directed attention on the basis of considerations of correspondence. In fact, our formula—in spite of the very different modes of symbolization and thought—must be considered formally identical with Kramers' secondary radiation formula. The important relationship of the secondary radiation coefficients to the spontaneous radiation coefficient a_{kn}, b_{kn} is shown and, in fact, the secondary radiation is described accurately even with respect to its state of polarization.

So far as concerns the absolute magnitude of the scattered radiation or the induced dipole moment, I should like to believe that it is also given correctly by Formula (23), although an error in the numerical factor is obviously within the range of possibility in view of the use of the heuristic hypothesis given above. In any case, the physical dimension is correct, for since the integrals of the squares of the eigenfunctions are normalized to unity, the a_{kn}, b_{kn} according to (18), (19), (21), and (22) are electric moments. The ratio of the induced dipole moment to the spontaneous moment is, if ν is remote from the emission frequency concerned, equal to an order of magnitude to the ratio of the additional potential energy Fa_{kn} to the "energy step" $E_k - E_n$.

. . . . .

§ 7. The Physical Significance of the Field Scalar

In § 2, the heuristic hypothesis of the electrodynamic significance of the field scalar ψ used previously for the *one*-electron problem was briefly generalized to any system of charged mass points and the prospect of a detailed description of this process held out. There we calculated the density of the electricity in any point of space as follows: *one* mass point is picked out, the coordination triplet which describes *its* position according to classical mechanics is fixed, $\psi\bar{\psi}$ is integrated over all the other system coordinates, and the result is multiplied by a certain constant, the "charge" of the selected mass point; the same procedure is carried out with every mass point (coordinate triplet) the same position being assigned each time to the particular mass point selected, namely the position of that point of *space* at which it is desired to know the electricity density. The latter is equal to the algebraic sum of the part-results.

This process, now, is equivalent to the following interpretation, which better shows the true significance of ψ. $\psi\bar{\psi}$ is a kind of *weight function* in the configuration space of the system. The *wave-mechanical* configuration of the system is a *superposition* of several—strictly *all*—kinematically possible point-mechanical configurations. Under these circumstances, each point-mechanical configuration enters with a certain *weight* in the true wave-mechanical configuration, the weight being given just by $\psi\bar{\psi}$. If you like paradoxes, you can say that the system is, as it were, simultaneously in all kinematically conceivable positions, but not "equally strongly" in all of them. In the case of macroscopic motions, the weight function contracts in practice to a small region of practically indistinguishable positions the centre of gravity of which in the configuration space covers macroscopically detectable distances. In the case of microscopic problems of motion the varying *distribution* over the region is *also* of interest, in any case, and for certain questions it is of *primary* interest.

This re-interpretation may appear shocking at first sight after we have previously spoken frequently in such an apparently concrete form of the "ψ-vibrations" as of something quite real. There is a basis of some tangible reality, however, even according to the present treatment—namely the very real electrodynamically active fluctuations of the electric space density. The ψ-function will be or give nothing more and nothing less than the fact that it permits the totality of these fluctuations to be mastered and reviewed mathematically by a single partial differential equation. It has been stressed repeatedly that the ψ-function itself cannot and must not in general be interpreted directly in terms of three-dimensional space, however much the one-electron problem leads towards this, since it is in fact, in general, a function in the configuration space and not in actual space.†

It will be desired of a weight function in the sense discussed above that its integral over the whole of configuration space should remain always normalized to one and the same invariable magnitude, preferably unity. In fact, one can easily be convinced that this is necessary so that, in accordance with the above definition, the total charge of the system remains constant. And, indeed, this requirement is obviously to be set for non-conservative systems also, since the charge of a system must naturally not change when, for example, a light wave is incident, lasts for a certain time, and then ceases again. (NB: This also applies to ionization processes. A separated particle is initially still to be reckoned with the system until the separation is also completed *logically*—by a division of the configuration space.)

The question now arises as to whether this *persistence of the normalization* to be required is actually guaranteed by modifying Equations (4″) of p. 154 to which ψ is subjected. If this were not the case, it would be fairly catastrophic for our whole conception. Fortunately, it is the case. Let us consider

$$\frac{d}{dt}\int \psi\bar{\psi}\varrho\, dx = \int \left(\psi\frac{\partial\bar{\psi}}{\partial t} + \bar{\psi}\frac{\partial\psi}{\partial t}\right)\varrho\, dx. \qquad (37)$$

Now ψ satisfies one of the two Equations (4″), and $\bar{\psi}$ therefore satisfies the other. Consequently, the preceding integral, apart from a multiplicative constant, becomes:

$$\int(\psi\,\nabla^2\bar{\psi} - \bar{\psi}\,\nabla^2\psi)\,\varrho\, dx = 2i\int(J\,\nabla^2 R - R\,\nabla^2 J)\,\varrho\, dx, \qquad (38)$$

in which

$$\psi = R + iJ$$

has been put for the moment. The integral (38) vanishes identically according to Green's law; the single condition that the functions R and J have to satisfy for this—to vanish sufficiently

† *Ann. d. Phys.* **79**, pp. 526, 754, 1926.

strongly at infinity—means physically nothing other than that the system considered is limited in practice to a *finite* range.

The above can be used somewhat differently if we integrate not directly over the whole of configuration space but merely change the temporal differential quotients of the weight function into a divergence by Green's transformation. This gives an insight into the flow behaviour—first of the weight function and through it of the electricity. Let us multiply the two equations

$$\frac{\partial\psi}{\partial t} = \frac{h}{4\pi i}\left(\nabla^2 - \frac{8\pi^2}{h^2}V\right)\psi,$$

$$\frac{\partial\bar{\psi}}{\partial t} = -\frac{h}{4\pi i}\left(\nabla^2 - \frac{8\pi^2}{h^2}V\right)\bar{\psi} \qquad (4'')$$

by $\varrho\bar{\psi}$ and by $\varrho\psi$, respectively, and add the results:

$$\frac{\partial}{\partial t}(\varrho\psi\bar{\psi}) = \frac{h}{4\pi i}\varrho\,(\bar{\psi}\,\nabla^2\psi - \psi\,\nabla^2\bar{\psi}). \qquad (39)$$

In order to carry out the transformation of the right-hand side in extenso, we must recall the explicit form of our multidimensional non-Euclidean Laplacian operator:†

$$\varrho\,\nabla^2 = \sum_k \frac{\partial}{\partial q_k}\left[\varrho T_{p_k}\left(q_l, \frac{\partial\psi}{\partial q_l}\right)\right]. \qquad (40)$$

By a slight rearrangement we then easily find:

$$\frac{\partial}{\partial t}(\varrho\psi\bar{\psi}) = \frac{h}{4\pi i}\sum_k \frac{\partial}{\partial q_k}\left[\varrho\bar{\psi}T_{p_k}\left(q_l, \frac{\partial\psi}{\partial q_l}\right) - \varrho\psi T_{p_k}\left(q_l, \frac{\partial\psi}{\partial q_l}\right)\right]. \qquad (41)$$

† *Ann. d. Phys.* **79**, p. 748, 1926, equation (31). The quantity there denoted by $\Delta_p^{-\frac{1}{2}}$ is our "density function" $\varrho(x)$ (e.g. $r^2 \sin\vartheta$ for a triplet of polar coordinates). T is the kinetic energy as a function of the position coordinates and *momenta*, and the index attached to T denotes the derivative with respect to a momentum coordinate.

In equations (31) and (32) of the paper cited, unfortunately the index k was used twice by an oversight, once as summation index and then again as a representative index in the argument of the functions.

The right-hand side appears as a divergence of a multidimensional real vector which is obviously to be interpreted as the *current density of the weight function* in the configuration space. Equation (41) is the *continuity equation* of the weight function.

From this we can obtain the *continuity equation of the electricity* and, in fact, such an equation applies individually for the charge density "arising from each individual mass point". Let us, for example, consider the α-th mass point, let its "charge" be e_α, its mass m_α, and its coordinate space be described, for the sake of simplicity, by Cartesian coordinates, $x_\alpha, y_\alpha, z_\alpha$. We denote the product of the differentials of the *other* coordinates by dx' for short. Let us integrate Equation (41) over them with *fixed* x_α, y_α, z_α. In this integration, the right-hand sides of all the members disappear except for three, and we obtain:

$$\begin{aligned}\frac{\partial}{\partial t}\left[e_\alpha \int \psi\bar{\psi}\, dx'\right] &= \frac{he_\alpha}{4\pi i m_\alpha}\left\{\frac{\partial}{\partial x_\alpha}\left[\int\left(\bar{\psi}\frac{\partial \psi}{\partial x_\alpha} - \psi\frac{\partial \bar{\psi}}{\partial x_\alpha}\right)dx'\right]\right. \\ &\qquad \left. + \frac{\partial}{\partial y_\alpha}\left[\int\left(\bar{\psi}\frac{\partial \psi}{\partial y_\alpha} - \psi\frac{\partial \bar{\psi}}{\partial y_\alpha}\right)dx'\right] + \cdots\right\} \\ &= \frac{he_\alpha}{4\pi i m_\alpha}\operatorname{div}_\alpha\left[\int(\bar{\psi}\operatorname{grad}_\alpha \psi - \psi \operatorname{grad}_\alpha \bar{\psi})\, dx'\right].\end{aligned} \tag{42}$$

In this equation, div and grad have the usual three-dimensional Euclidean significance and x_α, y_α, z_α are to be regarded as Cartesian coordinates of real space. The equation is the continuity equation of *that* charge density that "arises from the α-th mass point". If the others are formulated analogously and they are all added, we obtain the over-all continuity equation. It must of course be stressed that, as always in such cases, the conception of the integrals of the right-hand side as *components of the current density* is not absolutely necessary, since a divergence-free vector could come in.

To give an example, for the conservative *one*-electron problem, when ψ is given by

$$\psi = \sum_k c_k u_k e^{2\pi i \nu_k t + i\vartheta_k} \qquad (c_k, \vartheta_k \text{ real constants}) \tag{43}$$

we obtain as the *current density* J^-

$$J = \frac{he_1}{2\pi m_1} \sum_{(k,l)} c_k c_l (u_l \operatorname{grad} u_k - u_k \operatorname{grad} u_l) \times \sin [2\pi(v_k - v_l) t + \vartheta_k - \vartheta_l]. \tag{44}$$

It can be seen—and this holds generally for conservative systems —that if only a single eigenvibration is excited the current components disappear and the distribution of the electricity becomes constant with time; the latter can be seen directly, since $\psi\bar{\psi}$ is constant with time. This applies also if in fact several eigenvibrations are excited that all belong to the same eigenvalue. On the other hand, the current density then no longer need vanish, but a *stationary* current distribution may and will, in general, be present. Since in the unperturbed normal state one or the other situation occurs in any case, in a certain sense we may speak of a *return to electrostatic and magnetostatic atom models.* Consequently, the capability of the emission of radiation of the normal state in fact finds an astonishingly simple solution.

I hope and believe that the above discussions will prove to be useful for the elucidation for the magnetic properties of atoms and molecules and also for the elucidation of the flow of electricity in solids.

. . . . .

PAPER 6

The Interpretation of Kinematic and Mechanical Relationships according to the Quantum Theory†

By W. HEISENBERG

In this paper an attempt will be made to obtain bases for a quantum-theoretical mechanics based exclusively on relationships between quantities observable in principle.

IT IS well known that the formal rules that are generally used in the quantum theory for the calculation of observable quantities (e.g. the energy in the hydrogen atom) are often subjected to the serious objection that those rules contain as an essential constituent relationships between quantities that are apparently incapable of observation in principle (such as, for example, the position and the period of rotation of the electron) and that therefore those rules obviously lack any visualizable physical foundation, if we do not desire to continue to retain the hope that those so far unobservable quantities could later perhaps be made experimentally accessible. This hope could be regarded as justified if the rules mentioned were self-consistent and applicable to a definitely limited range of quantum-theoretical problems. However, experience shows that only the hydrogen atom and the Stark effect of this atom satisfy those formal rules of the quantum theory, but that even in the problem of the "crossed fields" (a hydrogen atom in electric and magnetic fields of different directions) serious difficulties arise, that the reaction of atoms to periodically varying fields can certainly not be

† *Zeitschrift für Physik*, **33**, 879, 1925.

described by the rules mentioned, and that, finally, an extension of the quantum rule to the treatment of atoms with several electrons has proved to be impossible. It has become customary to call this failure of the quantum-theoretical rules which were in fact characterized essentially by the use of classical mechanics, a deviation from classical mechanics. However, this terminology can hardly be regarded as appropriate when it is considered that even the (quite generally valid) Einstein-Bohr frequency condition represents such a complete denial of classical mechanics or, better, from the standpoint of the wave theory, of the kinematics at the basis of this mechanics, and even in the case of the simplest quantum-theoretical problems it is absolutely impossible to think of any validity of classical mechanics. In this state of affairs, it appears better to give up the hope of an observation of the previously unobservable quantities (such as the position and time of revolution of the electron) completely, and simultaneously, therefore, to grant that the partial agreement of the known quantum rules with experience is more or less fortuitous and to attempt to formulate a quantum-theoretical mechanics analogous to classical mechanics in which only relationships between observable quantities occur. Besides the frequency conditions, Kramers' dispersion theory† and the papers forming developments of this theory‡ can be regarded as the most important first steps to such a quantum-theoretical mechanics. Below we shall attempt to develop some new quantum mechanical relations and use them for the full treatment of some special problems. In this, we shall restrict ourselves to problems with one degree of freedom.

§ 1. In the classical theory, the radiation of an electron in motion $\left(\text{in the wave zone, i.e. } \boldsymbol{E} \sim \boldsymbol{H} \sim \frac{1}{r}\right)$ is not given by the

† H. A. Kramers, *Nature*, **113**, 673, 1924.

‡ M. Born, *Zs. f. Phys.* **26**, 379, 1924. H. A. Kramers and W. Heisenberg, *Zs. f. Phys.* **31**, 681, 1925. M. Born and P. Jordan *Zs. f. Phys.* (in the press).

expressions:

$$\boldsymbol{E} = \frac{e}{r^3c^2}[\boldsymbol{r} \wedge [\boldsymbol{r} \wedge \dot{\boldsymbol{v}}]],$$

$$\boldsymbol{H} = \frac{e}{r^2c^2}[\dot{\boldsymbol{v}} \wedge \boldsymbol{r}]$$

alone, but other terms come into a first approximation, e.g. those of the form

$$\frac{e}{rc^3}\dot{\boldsymbol{v}}\boldsymbol{v},$$

which can be called "quadrupole radiation" and to a still higher degree of approximation terms of, for example, the form

$$\frac{e}{rc^4}\dot{\boldsymbol{v}}\boldsymbol{v}^2.$$

In this way, the approximation can be taken as far as may be desired. (In the above expressions, $\boldsymbol{E}$, $\boldsymbol{H}$, denote the field strengths, e the charge of the electron, $\boldsymbol{r}$ the distance-vector of the electron from the point considered, and $\boldsymbol{v}$ the velocity of the electron.)

We may ask ourselves what these higher terms will be like in the quantum theory. Since in the classical theory the higher approximations can be calculated simply if the motion of the electron or its Fourier expansion is given, a similar situation will be expected in the quantum theory. This question has nothing to do with electrodynamics but it is, and this appears to us to be particularly important, of purely *kinematic* nature; we can represent it in the simplest form as follows: let a quantum-theoretical quantity taking the place of the position of the classical magnitude $x(t)$ be given; what quantum-theoretical quantity then takes the place of $x(t)^2$?

Before we can answer this question, we must remember that in quantum theory it was not possible to assign to the electron a point in space as a function of the time by means of observable quantities. However, an emission of radiation can be assigned to the electron even in quantum theory; this radiation is described in the first place by the frequencies that occur as functions of two variables—in the quantum theory in the form:

$$\nu(n, n-\alpha) = \frac{1}{h}\{W(n) - W(n-\alpha)\},$$

and in the classical theory in the form:

$$\nu(n, \alpha) = \alpha \cdot \nu(n) = \alpha \frac{1}{h} \frac{dW}{dn}.$$

(Here, nh is put equal to J, one of the canonical constants.)

We can write the combination relations as characteristic for the comparison of classical theory with quantum theory with respect to the frequencies:

Classical:

$$\nu(n, \alpha) + \nu(n, \beta) = \nu(n, \alpha + \beta).$$

Quantum theory:

$$\nu(n, n-\alpha) + \nu(n-\alpha, n-\alpha-\beta) = \nu(n, n-\alpha-\beta)$$

or

$$\nu(n-\beta, n-\alpha-\beta) + \nu(n, n-\beta) = \nu(n, n-\alpha-\beta).$$

In addition to the frequencies, the amplitudes are necessary to describe the radiation; the amplitudes may be regarded as complex vectors (each with six independent determining parts) and determine polarization and phase. These are also functions of the two variables n and α, so that the part of the radiation concerned is represented by the following expressions:

Quantum theory:

$$Re\{A(n, n-\alpha)\, e^{i\omega(n, n-\alpha)t}\}. \tag{1}$$

Classical:

$$Re\{A_\alpha(n)\, e^{i\omega(n)\,.\,\alpha t}\}. \tag{2}$$

The phase (included in A) does not appear at first sight to be associated with a physical significance in quantum theory, since in quantum theory the frequencies are in general not commensurable with their harmonics. However, we shall see immediately that the phase also has a definite significance in the quantum theory analogous to that in the classical theory. If we now consider a definite quantity $x(t)$ in the classical theory, it can be regarded as represented by a totality of quantities of the form

$$A_\alpha(n)\, e^{i\omega(n)\,.\,\alpha t},$$

which, according to whether the motion is periodical or not, when combined into a sum or an integral form $x(t)$:

$$\left.\begin{aligned} x(n, t) &= \sum_{-\infty}^{+\infty}{}_\alpha A_\alpha(n)\, e^{i\omega(n)\,.\,\alpha t} \\ \text{or} \quad & \\ x(n, t) &= \int_{-\infty}^{+\infty} A_\alpha(n)\, e^{i\omega(n)\alpha t}\, d\alpha. \end{aligned}\right\} \tag{2a}$$

Such a combination of the corresponding quantum-theoretical quantities does not appear to be possible without arbitrariness because of the equal claims of the quantities n and $n - \alpha$ and therefore appears meaningless: however, the totality of the quantities

$$A(n, n - \alpha)\, e^{i\omega(n,\, n-\alpha)t}$$

can indeed be regarded as representant of the quantity $x(t)$ and then it is possible to attempt to answer the question posed above: by what will the quantity $x(t)^2$ be represented?

Classically, the answer obviously runs as follows:

$$B_\beta(n)\, e^{i\omega(n)\beta t} = \sum_{-\infty}^{+\infty}{}_\alpha A_\alpha A_{\beta-\alpha}\, e^{i\omega(n)(\alpha+\beta-\alpha)t} \tag{3}$$

or

$$= \int_{-\infty}^{+\infty} A_\alpha A_{\beta-\alpha}\, e^{i\omega(n)(\alpha+\beta-\alpha)t}\, d\alpha, \tag{4}$$

so that

$$x(t)^2 = \sum_{-\infty}^{+\infty}{}_\beta B_\beta(n)\, e^{i\omega(n)\beta t} \tag{5}$$

or

$$= \int_{-\infty}^{+\infty} B_\beta(n)\, e^{i\omega(n)\beta t}\, d\beta. \tag{6}$$

For the quantum theory, the simplest and most natural assumption appears to be to replace Relations (3, 4) by the following:

$$B(n, n-\beta)\, e^{i\omega(n, n-\beta)t}$$

$$= \sum_{-\infty}^{+\infty}{}_{\alpha} A(n, n-\alpha)\, A(n-\alpha, n-\beta)\, e^{i\omega(n, n-\beta)t} \qquad (7)$$

and

$$= \int_{-\infty}^{+\infty} d\alpha A(n, n-\alpha)\, A(n-\alpha, n-\beta)\, e^{i\omega(n, n-\beta)t}, \qquad (8)$$

respectively, and in fact this type of formulation follows almost necessarily from the combination relation of the frequencies. If this assumption (7) and (8) is made, we also see that the phases of the quantum-theoretical A have a physical significance as great as in the classical theory: only the initial moment of time and therefore a phase constant common to all A is arbitrary and without physical significance, but the phase of the *individual* A is essentially included in the magnitude B.† A geometrical interpretation of such quantum-theoretical phase relationships in analogy with the classical theory appears hardly possible at the present time.

If, further, we seek the representant of the magnitude $x(t)^3$, we find without difficulty:

Classical:

$$C(n, \gamma) = \sum_{-\infty}^{+\infty} \sum_{-\infty}^{+\infty}{}_{\alpha,\beta} A_{\alpha}(n)\, A_{\beta}(n)\, A_{\gamma-\alpha-\beta}(n). \qquad (9)$$

Quantum theory:

$$C(n, n-\gamma) = \sum_{-\infty}^{+\infty} \sum_{-\infty}^{+\infty}{}_{\alpha,\beta} A(n, n-\alpha)\, A(n-\alpha, n-\alpha-\beta)$$

$$\times A(n-\alpha-\beta, n-\gamma) \qquad (10)$$

or the corresponding integrals.

† See also H. A. Kramers and W. Heisenberg, *loc. cit.* The phases are included essentially in the expression used there for the induced scattering moment.

All quantities of the form $x(t)^n$ can be represented in the quantum theory in a similar manner, and when any one function $f[x(t)]$ is given it is obviously always possible, if this function can be expanded in a power series in x, to find the quantum-theoretical analogue. However, a substantial difficulty arises if we consider two quantities $x(t)$, $y(t)$ and seek the product $x(t)y(t)$.

If $x(t)$ is characterized by A, and $y(t)$ by B, we obtain as the representation of $x(t) \cdot y(t)$:

Classical:

$$C_\beta(n) = \sum_{-\infty}^{+\infty}{}_\alpha A_\alpha(n)\, B_{\beta-\alpha}(n).$$

Quantum theory:

$$C(n, n-\beta) = \sum_{-\infty}^{+\infty}{}_\alpha A(n, n-\alpha)\, B(n-\alpha, n-\beta).$$

While classically $x(t) \cdot y(t)$ is always equal to $y(t)x(t)$, this need not be the case, in general, in the quantum theory. In special cases, e.g. in the formation of $x(t) \cdot x(t)^2$, this difficulty does not appear.

When, as in the question posed at the beginning of this section, it is a question of expressions of the form $v(t)\dot{v}(t)$, in the quantum theory $v\dot{v}$ must be replaced by $\dfrac{v\dot{v} + \dot{v}v}{2}$ in order to achieve the situation that $v\dot{v}$ appears as the differential quotient of $\dfrac{v^2}{2}$. Naturally, quantum-theoretical averages can always be given in a similar way, but these are still more highly hypothetical than Formulae (7) and (8).

Apart from the difficulty just sketched, formulae of type (7) and (8) are generally sufficient also for expressing the interaction of the electron in an atom in terms of the characteristic amplitudes of the electron.

§ 2. After these considerations on the kinematics of the quantum theory, we shall turn to the mechanical problem aimed at the determination of A, v, and W from the given forces in the system. In the previous theory, this problem was solved in two steps:

1. Integration of the equation of motion

$$\ddot{x} + f(x) = 0. \tag{11}$$

2. Determination of the constants for periodic motion by means of

$$\oint p\, dq = \oint m\dot{x}\, dx = J(=nh). \tag{12}$$

If we undertake the task of constructing a quantum-theoretical mechanics as analogous to classical mechanics as possible, it is a perfectly obvious matter to take over the equation of motion (11) directly into the quantum theory, it only being necessary—in order not to depart from the sure foundation of quantities observable in principle—to replace the quantities $\ddot{x}$ and $f(x)$ by their representants in the quantum theory known from § 1. In the classical theory, it is possible to seek the solution of (11) by writing x in Fourier series or Fourier integrals with undetermined coefficients (and frequencies); however, in general we then obtain an infinite number of equations with an infinite number of unknowns or integral equations which can be converted into simple recurrence formulae for the A only in special cases. In quantum theory, however, we are for the time being restricted to this type of solution since, as mentioned above, none of these functions $x(n, t)$ permits the definition of directly analogous quantum-theoretical functions.

This has the consequence that the quantum-theoretical solution of (11) can at present be performed only in the simplest cases. Before we go into such simple examples, the quantum-theoretical determination of the constant according to (12) may be given. We assume, therefore, that the (classical) motion is periodic:

$$x = \sum_{-\infty}^{+\infty}{}_{\alpha}\, a_{\alpha}(n)\, c^{i\alpha\omega_n t}; \tag{13}$$

then

$$m\dot{x} = m \sum_{-\infty}^{+\infty} a_{\alpha}(n) \cdot i\alpha\omega_n\, e^{i\alpha\omega_n t}$$

and $$\oint m\dot{x}\,dx = \oint m\dot{x}^2\,dt = 2\pi m \sum_{-\infty}^{+\infty}{}_{\alpha}\, a_{\alpha}(n)\, a_{-\alpha}(n)\,\alpha^2\omega_n.$$

Since, moreover, $a_{-\alpha}(n) = \bar{a}_{\alpha}(n)$ (x must be real), it follows that

$$\oint m\dot{x}^2\,dt = 2\pi m \sum_{-\infty}^{+\infty}{}_{\alpha}\, |a_{\alpha}(n)|^2\,\alpha^2\omega_n. \tag{14}$$

This phase integral has previously generally been put equal to an integral multiple of h, i.e. equal to nh; however, not only does such a condition fit into the mechanical calculation in a very forced manner but it also appears, even from the previous standpoint, to be arbitrary in the sense of the correspondence principle, for from the point of view of correspondence the J are determined, apart from an additive constant, as integral multiples of h and the following expression must naturally appear in place of (14):

$$\frac{d}{dn}(nh) = \frac{d}{dn}\cdot\oint m\dot{x}^2\,dt,$$

i.e.

$$h = 2\pi m\cdot\sum_{-\infty}^{+\infty}{}_{\alpha}\,\alpha\,\frac{d}{dn}(\alpha\omega_n\cdot|a_{\alpha}|^2). \tag{15}$$

However, such a condition fixes the a_{α} except for a constant, and this uncertainty has empirically given rise to difficulties in the appearance of half-odd-integral quantum numbers.

If we seek a quantum-theoretical relationship between observable quantities corresponding to (14) and (15), the lacking unambiguity reappears spontaneously.

In fact, it is only Equation (15) that possesses a simple quantum-theoretical transformation connected with Kramers' dispersion theory:†

$$h = 4\pi m \sum_{0}^{\infty}{}_{\alpha}\{|a(n, n+\alpha)|^2\,\omega(n, n+\alpha) - |a(n, n-\alpha)|^2\,\omega(n, n-\alpha)\}, \tag{16}$$

† This relation has previously been given on the basis of considerations of dispersion by W. Kuhn, *Zs. f. Phys.* **33**, 408, 1925, and by Thomas, *Naturw.* **13**, 1925.

but this relation is sufficient here for the unambiguous determination of the a, for the initially undetermined constant in the quantities a is determined directly by the condition that it is to give a ground state from which no more radiation takes place: if the ground state is denoted by n_0, in all cases we shall have

$$a(n_0, n_0 - \alpha) = 0 \quad (\text{for } \alpha > 0).$$

The question of half-odd-integral or integral quantization can therefore probably not arise in a quantum-theoretical mechanics using only relationships between observable quantities.

Equations (11) and (16) together contain, when they can be solved, a complete determination of not only the frequencies and energies but also the quantum-theoretical transition probabilities. The actual mathematical operations, however, can only be carried out at the moment in the simplest cases: a special complication also arises in many systems such as, for example, in the hydrogen atom, by virtue of the fact that the solutions correspond sometimes to periodic and sometimes to aperiodic motions, which has the consequence that the quantum-theoretical theories (7) and (8) and Equation (16) always decompose into a sum and an integral. A separation into "periodic and aperiodic motions" can, in general, not be carried out by quantum mechanics.

Nevertheless, Equations (11) and (16) could be regarded, at least in principle, as a satisfactory solution of the mechanical problem if it could be shown that this solution agrees or does not contradict the quantum-mechanical relationships known at the present time and that, therefore, a small perturbation of a mechanical problem gives rise to additional terms in the energy or in the frequencies which precisely correspond to the expressions found by Kramers and Born—in contrast to those that the classical theory would yield. In addition, we must investigate whether, in general, an energy integral $m\frac{\dot{x}^2}{2} + U(x) = \text{const.}$ corresponds to Equation (11), even in the quantum-theoretical form proposed here and whether—in the same way as the relation $\nu = \dfrac{\partial W}{\partial J}$ holds in classical mechanics—the energy so obtained satisfies the condition: $\Delta W = h\nu$. Only a general answer to this question could show the inner relationship of the quantum-mechanical experiments that have been carried out and lead to a quantum mechanics consequently operating only with observable quantities. Apart from a general relationship between Kramers' dispersion formula and Equations (11) and (16), we can answer the questions posed above only in the quite special cases soluble by simple recurrence.

. . . . .

§ 3. As the simplest example we shall treat the anharmonic oscillator:

$$\ddot{x} + \omega_0^2 x + \lambda x^2 = 0. \tag{17}$$

Classically, this equation can be satisfied by a relation of the form

$$x = \lambda a_0 + a_1 \cos \omega t + \lambda a_2 \cos 2\omega t + \lambda^2 a_3 \cos 3\omega t \ldots + \lambda^{\tau-1} a_\tau \cos \tau\omega t + \cdots$$

in which the a are power series in λ beginning with a term not containing λ. Let us seek an analogous relation in the quantum theory and represent x by terms of the form

$$\lambda a(n, n); \quad a(n, n-1) \cos \omega(n, n-1)\, t;$$
$$\lambda a(n, n-2) \cos \omega(n, n-2)\, t;$$
$$\ldots \lambda^{\tau-1}\, a(n, n-\tau) \cos \omega(n, n-\tau)\, t \ldots$$

The recurrence formulae for determining the a and ω are (except for terms of the order λ) according to Equations (3), and (4) or (7) and (8):

Classical:

$$\left.\begin{aligned} \omega_0^2 a_0(n) + \frac{a_1^2(n)}{2} &= 0; \\ -\omega^2 + \omega_0^2 &= 0; \\ (-4\omega^2 + \omega_0^2)\, a_2(n) + \frac{a_1^2}{2} &= 0; \\ (-9\omega^2 + \omega_0^2)\, a_3(n) + a_1 a_2 &= 0; \\ \ldots\ldots\ldots\ldots\ldots\ldots \end{aligned}\right\} \tag{18}$$

Quantum theory:

$$\left.\begin{array}{r}
\omega_0^2 a_0(n) + \dfrac{a^2(n+1,n) + a^2(n,n-1)}{4} = 0; \\
-\omega^2(n,n-1) + \omega_0^2 = 0; \\
(-\omega^2(n,n-2) + \omega_0^2)\, a(n,n-2) \\
+ \dfrac{a(n,n-1)\, a(n-1,n-2)}{2} = 0; \\
(-\omega^2(n,n-3) + \omega_0^2)\, a(n,n-3) \\
+ \dfrac{a(n,n-1)\, a(n-1,n-3)}{2} \\
+ \dfrac{a(n,n-2)\, a(n-2,n-3)}{2} = 0. \\
\cdots\cdots\cdots\cdots\cdots\cdots\cdots\cdots\cdots
\end{array}\right\} \quad (19)$$

In addition to this we have the quantum condition:

Classical ($J = nh$):

$$1 = 2\pi m \frac{d}{dJ} \sum_{-\infty}^{+\infty} \tau^3 \frac{|a_\tau|^2 \omega}{4}.$$

Quantum theory:

$$h = \pi m \sum_{0}^{\infty} [|a(n+\tau,n)|^2 \omega(n+\tau,n) - |a(n,n-\tau)|^2 \omega(n,n-\tau)].$$

To a first approximation, this gives both in the classical and in the quantum theory:

$$a_1^2(n) \quad \text{or} \quad a^2(n,n-1) = \frac{(n + \text{const})\, h}{\pi m \omega_0}. \qquad (20)$$

In quantum theory, the constant in (20) can be determined by the condition that in the ground state $a(n_0, n_0 - 1)$ is to be zero. If we number the n so that n in the ground state is zero, i.e. $n_0 = 0$, it follows that

$$a^2(n,n-1) = \frac{nh}{\pi m \omega_0}.$$

From the recurrence equations (18) it then follows that in the classical theory a_τ (to a first approximation in λ) becomes of the form $\varkappa(\tau)\, n^{\tau/2}$, where $\varkappa(\tau)$ represents a factor independent of n. In quantum theory, we obtain from (19)

$$a(n, n-\tau) = \varkappa(\tau) \sqrt{\frac{n!}{(n-\tau)!}}, \tag{21}$$

in which $\varkappa(\tau)$ represents the same n-independent proportionality factor. For large values of n, of course, the value of a_τ according to the quantum theory passes asymptotically into the classical value.

For the energy, it is an obvious matter to seek the classical relation

$$\frac{m\dot{x}^2}{2} + m\omega_0^2 \frac{x^2}{2} + \frac{m\lambda}{3} x^3 = W$$

which in the approximation used in the calculations here is also actually constant in the quantum theory and has the value according to (19), (20), and (21) of:

Classical:

$$W = \frac{nh\omega_0}{2\pi}. \tag{22}$$

Quantum theory [according to (7) and (8)]:

$$W = \frac{(n + \frac{1}{2})\, h\omega_0}{2\pi} \tag{23}$$

(except for terms of the order of λ^2).

According to this idea, therefore, even with the harmonic oscillator the energy cannot be represented by "classical mechanics", i.e. by (22), but has the form (23).

The more accurate calculation including the higher approximations in W, a, and ω will be carried out with the simpler example of the anharmonic oscillator of the type:

$$\ddot{x} + \omega_0^2 x + \lambda x^3 = 0.$$

Classically, here we can put:

$$x = a_1 \cos \omega t + \lambda a_3 \cos 3\omega t + \lambda^2 a_5 \cos 5\omega t + \cdots,$$

analogously, in the quantum theory we try to write

$$a(n, n-1) \cos \omega(n, n-1)\, t; \quad \lambda a(n, n-3) \cos \omega(n, n-3)\, t.$$

The quantities a are again power series in λ, the first term of which, as in (21), has the form:

$$a(n, n-\tau) = \varkappa(\tau) \sqrt{\frac{n!}{(n-\tau)!}},$$

as we find by calculating the equations corresponding to Equations (18) and (19).

If the calculation of ω and a is carried out according to (18) and (19) to the approximation λ^2 or λ, we obtain:

$$\omega(n, n-1) = \omega_0 + \lambda \cdot \frac{3nh}{8\pi\omega_0^2 m} - \lambda^2 \cdot \frac{3h^2}{256\omega_0^5 m^2 \pi^2} (17n^2 + 7) + \cdots \tag{24}$$

$$a(n, n-1) = \sqrt{\frac{nh}{\pi\omega_0 m}} \left(1 - \lambda \frac{3nh}{16\pi\omega_0^3 m} + \cdots\right), \tag{25}$$

$$a(n, n-3) = \frac{1}{32} \sqrt{\frac{h^3}{\pi^3 \omega_0^7 m^3} n(n-1)(n-2)} \times \left(1 - \lambda \frac{39(n-1)h}{32\pi\omega_0^3 m}\right). \tag{26}$$

The energy, which is defined as the constant term in

$$m\frac{\dot{x}^2}{2} + m\omega_0^2 \frac{x^2}{2} + \frac{m\lambda}{4} x^4$$

(I have been unable to show generally that the periodic terms are actually all zero, but in the terms calculated this was in fact the case), comes to

$$W = \frac{(n+\frac{1}{2})h\omega_0}{2\pi} + \lambda \frac{3(n^2 + n + \frac{1}{2})h^2}{8 \cdot 4\pi^2\omega_0^2 \cdot m} - \lambda^2 \frac{h^3}{512\pi^3\omega_0^5 m^2} \left(17n^3 + \frac{51}{2}n^2 + \frac{59}{2}n + \frac{21}{2}\right). \tag{27}$$

This energy can also be calculated by the Kramers–Born process by regarding the term $\frac{m\lambda}{4}x^4$ as the perturbing term to the harmonic oscillator. In fact, we then come back again to the result (27), which appears to me to be a remarkable point in favour of the quantum-mechanical equations used as a basis. Moreover, the energy calculated according to (27) satisfies the formula [cf. (24)]:

$$\frac{\omega(n, n-1)}{2\pi} = \frac{1}{h} \cdot [W(n) - W(n-1)],$$

which is again to be regarded as a necessary condition for the possibility of a determination of the transition probabilities corresponding to Equations (11) and (16).

Whether a method for determining quantum-theoretical data by means of relations between observable quantities such as those proposed here could in fact be regarded as satisfactory in principle or whether this method still represents a much too coarse attack on the physical and at first sight obviously very complicated problem of a quantum-theoretical mechanics will only be shown by a more far-reaching mathematical investigation of the methods used very superficially here.

PAPER 7

Quantum Mechanics†

M. BORN and P. JORDAN

The relations recently given by Heisenberg are (at least for systems of one degree of freedom) developed into a systematic theory of quantum mechanics. The mathematical apparatus used is matrix calculation. After this has been set out briefly, the mechanical equations of motion are derived from a variational principle and proof is given that, on the basis of Heisenberg's quantum conditions, the energy law and Bohr's frequency condition follow from the mechanical equations. The question of the unambiguity of the solution and the significance of the phases in the partial vibrations is discussed on the basis of the anharmonic oscillator. The conclusion consists of an attempt to introduce the laws of the electromagnetic field into the new theory.

Introduction

The relations for a new kinematics and mechanics, recently given by Heisenberg‡ in this Journal, which correspond to the basic requirements of the quantum theory, appear to us to be of great significance. They represent an attempt to justify the new facts not by a more or less artificial and forced adaptation of the customary old concepts but by the creation of a new truly suitable system of concepts. Heisenberg has given an account of the physical ideas that have guided him in this in such a clear manner that any supplementary remarks appear superfluous.

† *Zeitschrift für Physik*, **34**, 858, 1925.

‡ W. Heisenberg, *Zs. f. Phys.* **33**, 879, 1925 (see this volume, p. 168).

However, in the formal mathematical respect his arguments are, as he stresses himself, only in the initial stages. He has illustrated his hypotheses only with simple examples and has not advanced to a general theory. Favoured by the circumstance that we were able to gain a knowledge of his arguments even in the nascent state, after the conclusion of his investigations we made an attempt to clarify the mathematical-formal content of his relations, and we give some of our results here. They show that it is in fact possible to erect from the foundations given by Heisenberg the structure of a closed mathematical theory of quantum mechanics in remarkably close analogy to classical mechanics, but taking into account the features characterizing quantum phenomena.

In this process, we first limit ourselves, with Heisenberg, to systems of *one degree of freedom*, of which we assume that —speaking classically—they are periodic.

The mathematical basis of Heisenberg's treatment is the *multiplication law* of quantum-theoretical quantities, which he discovered by an ingenious consideration of correspondence. The shape of his formalism that we give here is based on the observation that this rule is nothing other than the law of the *multiplication of matrices*, which is well known to mathematicians. The quadratic scheme (with discrete or continuous indices) infinite in two directions, the so-called *matrix*, is the representant of a physical quantity which is given in the classical theory as a function of the time. The mathematical method of the new puantum mechanics is therefore characterized by the use of a *matrix analysis* in place of the usual numerical analysis.

. . . . .

Chapter 1. Matrix Calculation

§ 1. Elementary operations. Functions

We calculate with quadratic infinite *matrices*, which we shall denote here by letters in heavy type, while letters in light type will always denote ordinary numbers:

$$\boldsymbol{a} = (a(nm)) = \begin{pmatrix} a(00) & a(01) & a(02) \dots \\ a(10) & a(11) & a(12) \dots \\ a(20) & a(21) & a(22) \\ \dots & \dots & \dots \end{pmatrix}$$

. . . . .

We call that matrix the diagonal elements of which agree with those of $\boldsymbol{a}$, while all other elements are zero, the "*mean value*" of a matrix:

$$\bar{\boldsymbol{a}} = (\delta_{nm} a(nn)). \tag{8}$$

The sum of the diagonal elements will be called the "diagonal sum of the matrix $\boldsymbol{a}$" and will be denoted by $D(\boldsymbol{a})$:

$$D(\boldsymbol{a}) = \sum_n a(nn). \tag{9}$$

. . . . .

§ 2. Symbolic differentiation

A process of calculation much used later, which we shall consider in more detail here, will be called the *differentiation* of a matrix function. However, it must be noted that this process possesses similar properties to differentiation in ordinary analysis only in certain points. For example, here the product rule of the differentiation or the rule for the differentiation of a function of a function no longer has general validity. Only when all the matrices present commute with one another do all the rules of conventional analysis apply to this differentiation.

Let

$$\boldsymbol{y} = \prod_{m=1}^{s} \boldsymbol{x}_{l_m} = \boldsymbol{x}_{l_1} \boldsymbol{x}_{l_2} \dots \boldsymbol{x}_{l_s}. \tag{13}$$

We define

$$\frac{\partial \boldsymbol{y}}{\partial \boldsymbol{x}_k} = \sum_{r=1}^{s} \delta_{l_r k} \prod_{m=r+1}^{s} \boldsymbol{x}_{l_m} \prod_{m=1}^{m=r-1} \boldsymbol{x}_{l_m}, \quad \begin{cases} \delta_{jk} = 0 & \text{for} \quad j \neq k, \\ \delta_{kk} = 1. \end{cases} \tag{14}$$

In words, this rule runs: regard all the factors in the given product as written *individually* (i.e., for example, not $x_1^3 x_2^2$, but $x_1 x_1 x_1 x_2 x_2$); select any factor x_k and form the product of all the factors following it and all the factors preceding it (in this sequence). The sum of all the members formed in this way is the differential quotient of the product with respect to this x_k.

Some examples may illustrate the process:

$$y = x^n, \qquad \frac{dy}{dx} = nx^{n-1},$$

$$y = x_1^n x_2^m, \qquad \frac{\partial y}{\partial x_1} = x_1^{n-1} x_2^m + x_1^{n-2} x_2^m x_1 + \cdots + x_2^m x_1^{n-1},$$

$$y = x_1^2 x_2 x_1 x_3, \qquad \frac{\partial y}{\partial x_1} = x_1 x_2 x_1 x_3 + x_2 x_1 x_3 x_1 + x_3 x_1^2 x_2.$$

Furthermore, we require

$$\frac{\partial(y_1 + y_2)}{\partial x_k} = \frac{\partial y_1}{\partial x_k} + \frac{\partial y_2}{\partial x_k}, \tag{15}$$

and in this way the derivative $\frac{\partial x}{\partial y}$ defined for the most general analytical functions y.

With these definitions and that of the diagonal sum (9), the following relation holds:

$$\frac{\partial D(y)}{\partial x_k(nm)} = \frac{\partial y}{\partial x_k}(mn), \tag{16}$$

in which the right-hand side contains the mn component of the matrix $\frac{\partial y}{\partial x_k}$. This relation can also be used to define the derivative $\frac{\partial y}{\partial x_k}$. To prove (16) it is obviously sufficient to consider a function y of the form (13). From (14) and (3),

$$\frac{\partial y}{\partial x_k}(mn) = \sum_{r=1}^{s} \delta_{l_r k} \sum_{\tau} \prod_{p=r+1}^{s} x_{l_p}(\tau_p \tau_{p+1}) \prod_{p=1}^{r-l} x_{l_p}(\tau_p \tau_{p+1});$$

$$\tau_{r+1} = m, \qquad \tau_{s+1} = \tau_1, \qquad \tau_r = n. \tag{17}$$

On the other hand, from (3) and (9) we obtain:

$$\frac{\partial D(y)}{\partial x_k(mn)} = \sum_{r=1}^{s} \delta_{l_r k} \sum_{\tau} \prod_{p=1}^{r-1} x_{l_p}(\tau_p \tau_{p+1}) \prod_{p=r+1}^{s} x_{l_p}(\tau_p \tau_{p+1});$$

$$\tau_1 = \tau_{s+1}, \qquad \tau_r = n, \qquad \tau_{r+1} = m. \tag{17'}$$

A comparison of (17) and (17′) gives (16).

Just at this point we may stress a fact that is important later and which can be read from the definition (14): *The partial derivatives of a product are invariant with respect to cyclic permutations of the factors.* In view of (16), this rule can also be deduced from (10).

To conclude these preliminaries, a few words will be devoted to the functions $\boldsymbol{g}(\boldsymbol{pq})$ of *two* variables. For

$$\boldsymbol{y} = \boldsymbol{p}^s \boldsymbol{q}^r \tag{18}$$

we have according to (14)

$$\frac{\partial \boldsymbol{y}}{\partial \boldsymbol{p}} = \sum_{l=1}^{s-1} \boldsymbol{p}^{s-1-l} \boldsymbol{q}^r \boldsymbol{p}^l, \qquad \frac{\partial \boldsymbol{y}}{\partial \boldsymbol{q}} = \sum_{j=1}^{r-1} \boldsymbol{q}^{r-1-j} \boldsymbol{p}^s \boldsymbol{q}^j. \tag{18'}$$

The most general function $\boldsymbol{g}(\boldsymbol{pq})$ to be considered is to be represented according to § 1 by a linear combination of terms

$$\boldsymbol{z} = \prod_{j=1}^{k} (\boldsymbol{p}^{s_j} \boldsymbol{q}^{r_j}). \tag{19}$$

With the abbreviation

$$\boldsymbol{P}_l = \prod_{j=l+1}^{k} (\boldsymbol{p}^{s_j} \boldsymbol{q}^{r_j}) \prod_{j=1}^{l-1} (\boldsymbol{p}^{s_j} \boldsymbol{q}^{r_j}) \tag{20}$$

it is possible to write the derivatives

$$\left.\begin{aligned} \frac{\partial \boldsymbol{z}}{\partial \boldsymbol{p}} &= \sum_{l=1}^{k} \sum_{m=0}^{s_l-1} \boldsymbol{p}^{s_l-1-m} \boldsymbol{q}^{r_l} \boldsymbol{P}_l \boldsymbol{p}^m, \\ \frac{\partial \boldsymbol{z}}{\partial \boldsymbol{q}} &= \sum_{l=1}^{k} \sum_{m=0}^{s_l-1} \boldsymbol{q}^{r_l-1-m} \boldsymbol{P}_l \boldsymbol{p}^{s_l} \boldsymbol{q}^m. \end{aligned}\right\} \tag{21}$$

An important consequence can be derived from these equations. Let us consider the matrices

$$\boldsymbol{d}_1 = \boldsymbol{q}\frac{\partial z}{\partial \boldsymbol{q}} - \frac{\partial z}{\partial \boldsymbol{q}}\boldsymbol{p}, \qquad \boldsymbol{d}_2 = \boldsymbol{p}\frac{\partial z}{\partial \boldsymbol{p}} - \frac{\partial z}{\partial \boldsymbol{p}}\boldsymbol{p}. \tag{22}$$

According to (21),

$$\boldsymbol{d}_1 = \sum_{l=1}^{k}(\boldsymbol{q}^{r_l}\boldsymbol{P}_l\boldsymbol{p}^{s_l} - \boldsymbol{P}_l\boldsymbol{p}^{s_l}\boldsymbol{q}^{r_l}),$$

$$\boldsymbol{d}_2 = \sum_{l=1}^{k}(\boldsymbol{p}^{s_l}\boldsymbol{q}^{r_l}\boldsymbol{P}_l - \boldsymbol{q}^{r_l}\boldsymbol{P}_l\boldsymbol{p}^{s_l}),$$

and from this it follows that

$$\boldsymbol{d}_1 + \boldsymbol{d}_2 = \sum_{l=1}^{k}(\boldsymbol{p}^{s_l}\boldsymbol{q}^{r_l}\boldsymbol{P}_l - \boldsymbol{P}_l\boldsymbol{p}^{s_l}\boldsymbol{q}^{r_l}).$$

Here, the second member of one term cancels out the first member of the following term, and the first and last members of the whole sum cancel one another. Thus

$$\boldsymbol{d}_1 + \boldsymbol{d}_2 = 0. \tag{23}$$

Because it is linear in z, this relation holds not only for expressions z of the form (19) but also for any analytical function $g(\boldsymbol{pq})$.†

To conclude this brief account of matrix analysis, we shall now prove the law: *any matrix equation*

$$F(\boldsymbol{x}_1, \boldsymbol{x}_2, \dots \boldsymbol{x}_r) = 0$$

remains correct when the same permutation of all rows and of all columns is carried out in all argument matrices $\boldsymbol{x}_j$. For this it is obviously sufficient to show that for two matrices $\boldsymbol{a}$, $\boldsymbol{b}$ that are transformed into $\boldsymbol{a}'$, $\boldsymbol{b}'$ by this operation, the invariance

$$\boldsymbol{a}' + \boldsymbol{b}' = (\boldsymbol{a} + \boldsymbol{b})', \qquad \boldsymbol{a}'\boldsymbol{b}' = (\boldsymbol{ab})'$$

holds, where the right-hand sides of these matrices mean that they arise from $\boldsymbol{a} + \boldsymbol{b}$ and $\boldsymbol{ab}$ by those permutations.

† More generally, for functions of r variables

$$\sum_r\left(\boldsymbol{x}_r\frac{\partial g}{\partial \boldsymbol{x}_r} - \frac{\partial g}{\partial \boldsymbol{x}_r}\boldsymbol{x}_r\right) = 0.$$

We give this proof by replacing the operation of permutation by multiplication with a suitable matrix.†

Let us write a permutation

$$\begin{pmatrix} 0 & 1 & 2 & 3 & \dots \\ k_0 & k_1 & k_2 & k_3 & \dots \end{pmatrix} = \begin{pmatrix} n \\ k_n \end{pmatrix}.$$

To this we assign the *permutation matrix*

$$\boldsymbol{p} = (p(nm)), \qquad p(nm) = \begin{cases} 1 & \text{for} \quad m = k_n \\ 0 & \text{otherwise.} \end{cases}$$

Let the transposed matrix of $\boldsymbol{p}$ be

$$\tilde{\boldsymbol{p}} = (\tilde{p}(nm)), \qquad \tilde{p}(nm) = \begin{cases} 1 & \text{for} \quad n = k_m \\ 0 & \text{otherwise.} \end{cases}$$

Multiplication of the two gives

$$\boldsymbol{p}\tilde{\boldsymbol{p}} = \left(\sum_k p(nk)\,\tilde{p}(km)\right) = (\delta_{nm}) = 1,$$

since both factors $p(nk)$ and $\tilde{p}(km)$ are only simultaneously different from zero when $k = k_n = k_m$, and therefore $n = m$. Consequently, $\tilde{\boldsymbol{p}}$ is the reciprocal of $\boldsymbol{p}$:

$$\tilde{\boldsymbol{p}} = \boldsymbol{p}^{-1}.$$

Now let $\boldsymbol{a}$ be an arbitrary matrix, then

$$\boldsymbol{pa} = \left(\sum_k p(nk)\,a(km)\right) = (a(k_n, m))$$

is a matrix which arises from $\boldsymbol{a}$ by the permutation $\begin{pmatrix} n \\ k_n \end{pmatrix}$ of the rows, and likewise

$$\boldsymbol{ap}^{-1} = \left(\sum_k a(nk)\,\tilde{p}(km)\right) = (a(n, k_m))$$

† The proof selected here possesses the advantage that it shows the close relationship of the permutations with an important class of general transformations of matrices. The correctness of the law in question can, however, also be deduced directly from the observation that in the definition of the *equality* and the *addition* and *multiplication* of matrices no use is made of the order in which the rows or columns occur.

is the matrix arising from the permutation of the columns. One and the same permutation applied to rows and columns therefore yields the matrix

$$\boldsymbol{a}' = \boldsymbol{pap}^{-1}.$$

If follows from this directly that:

$$\boldsymbol{a}' + \boldsymbol{b}' = \boldsymbol{p}(\boldsymbol{a} + \boldsymbol{b})\,\boldsymbol{p}^{-1} = (\boldsymbol{a} + \boldsymbol{b})',$$

$$\boldsymbol{a}'\boldsymbol{b}' = \boldsymbol{pabp}^{-1} = (\boldsymbol{ab}'),$$

which proves our statement.

It can also be seen that no sequence or rank order of the elements can ever be determined by matrix equations.

Moreover, the much more general law that every matrix equation is invariant with respect to transformations of the form

$$\boldsymbol{a}' = \boldsymbol{bab}^{-1},$$

where $\boldsymbol{b}$ is *any* matrix, is obviously valid. We shall, of course, see later that this is no longer necessarily correct for matrix differential equations.

Chapter 2. Dynamics

§ 3. The Basic Laws

The dynamic system is to be described by the *coordinate* $\boldsymbol{q}$ and the momentum $\boldsymbol{p}$. They will be formulated as matrices

$$\boldsymbol{q} = \left(q(nm)\,e^{2\pi i\nu(nm)t}\right), \qquad \boldsymbol{p} = \left(p(nm)\,e^{2\pi i\nu(nm)t}\right). \tag{24}$$

In this, the $\nu(nm)$ denote the quantum-theoretical frequencies which belong to the transitions between the states with the *quantum numbers n* and *m*. The matrices (24) will be *Hermitian*, i.e. on transposition of the matrices each component will change to its conjugate complex, and this will in fact hold for all real t. We therefore have

$$q(nm)\,q(mn) = |q(nm)|^2 \tag{25}$$

and

$$\nu(nm) = -\,\nu(mn). \tag{26}$$

If $\boldsymbol{q}$ is a *Cartesian* coordinate, the quantity (25) is determinative for the probabilities of the $n \rightleftarrows m$ transitions.

We shall also require that

$$\nu(jk) + \nu(kl) + \nu(lj) = 0. \tag{27}$$

Together with (26), this can be expressed as follows: there are quantities W_n such that

$$h\nu(nm) = W_n - W_m. \tag{28}$$

From this it follows, with (2) and (3), that a function $g(\boldsymbol{p}, \boldsymbol{q})$ can always be written in the form

$$\boldsymbol{g} = \left(g(nm)\, e^{2\pi i\nu(nm)t}\right) \tag{29}$$

and, in fact, in this process the matrix $(g(nm))$ arises through just the same process from the matrices $(q(nm))$, $(p(nm))$ as that through which $\boldsymbol{g}$ was obtained from $\boldsymbol{q}, \boldsymbol{p}$. Consequently, instead of the method of (24), which will be abandoned from this point onwards, we can use the shorter mode of writing

$$\boldsymbol{q} = (q(nm)), \quad \boldsymbol{p} = (p(nm)). \tag{30}$$

As the time derivative of the matrix $\boldsymbol{g} = (g(nm))$ we obtain, if we once again bear (24) or (29) in mind, the matrix

$$\dot{\boldsymbol{g}} = 2\pi i(\nu(nm)\, g(nm)). \tag{31}$$

If, as we shall assume, $\nu(nm) \neq 0$ for $n \neq m$, $\dot{\boldsymbol{g}} = 0$ means that $\boldsymbol{g}$ is a diagonal matrix with $g(nm) = \delta_{nm} g(nm)$.

A differential equation $\dot{\boldsymbol{g}} = \boldsymbol{a}$ is invariant with respect to the process in which the rows and columns of all the matrices and the numbers W_n of them are subjected to permutation. In order to see this, let us consider the diagonal matrix

$$\boldsymbol{W} = (\delta_{nm} W_n);$$

then

$$\boldsymbol{W}\boldsymbol{g} = \left(\sum_k \delta_{nk} W_n g(km)\right) = (W_n g(nm)),$$

$$\boldsymbol{g}\boldsymbol{W} = \left(\sum_k g(nk)\, \delta_{km} W_k\right) = (W_m g(nm)),$$

and therefore from (31)

$$\dot{\boldsymbol{g}} = \frac{2\pi i}{h}((W_n - W_m)\, g(nm)) = \frac{2\pi i}{h}(\boldsymbol{Wg} - \boldsymbol{gW}).$$

If, now, $\boldsymbol{p}$ is a permutation matrix, the transformed

$$\boldsymbol{W}' = \boldsymbol{pWp}^{-1} = (\delta_{n_k m} W_{n_k})$$

is the diagonal matrix with the permuted W_n in the diagonal. We therefore have

$$\boldsymbol{p}\dot{\boldsymbol{g}}\boldsymbol{p}^{-1} = \frac{2\pi i}{h}(\boldsymbol{W}'\boldsymbol{g}' - \boldsymbol{g}'\boldsymbol{W}') = \dot{\boldsymbol{g}}',$$

where $\boldsymbol{g}' = \boldsymbol{pgp}^{-1}$, and $\dot{\boldsymbol{g}}'$ denotes the derivative of $\boldsymbol{g}'$ with respect to time formed according to Rule (31) with permuted W_n.

The rows and columns of $\dot{\boldsymbol{g}}$ therefore undergo the same permutations as those of $\boldsymbol{g}$, and our statement follows from this.

It must be noted that a corresponding law does *not* apply to any transformation of the form $\boldsymbol{a}' = \boldsymbol{bab}^{-1}$, since with such transformations $\boldsymbol{W}'$ is no longer a diagonal matrix. In spite of this difficulty, an accurate study of these general transformations appears indispensable to us, since it promises an insight into the deeper relationships of the new theory; we shall come back to this later.

For the case of a Hamiltonian function of the form

$$\boldsymbol{H} = \frac{1}{2m}\boldsymbol{p}^2 + U(\boldsymbol{q})$$

we shall assume, with Heisenberg, that the *equations of motion* read just like the classical equations, so that with the symbolism of § 2 we can write:

$$\left.\begin{aligned} \dot{\boldsymbol{q}} &= \frac{\partial \boldsymbol{H}}{\partial \boldsymbol{p}} = \frac{1}{m}\boldsymbol{p}, \\ \dot{\boldsymbol{p}} &= -\frac{\partial \boldsymbol{H}}{\partial \boldsymbol{q}} = -\frac{\partial \boldsymbol{U}}{\partial \boldsymbol{q}}. \end{aligned}\right\} \qquad (32)$$

An attempt will be made by a treatment based on correspondence, to determine appropriate equations of motion also for the general case of any Hamiltonian function $\boldsymbol{H}(\boldsymbol{p}, \boldsymbol{q})$. This is necessary for relativistic mechanics and particularly for the treatment of the motion of electrons under the additional action of magnetic fields, since in the latter case the function $\boldsymbol{H}$, with Cartesian coordinates, can no longer be represented as the sum of two functions one of which depends only on the momenta and the other only on the coordinates.

Classically, the equations of motion can be derived from the principle of least action

$$\int_{t_0}^{t_1} L\, dt = \int_{t_0}^{t_1} \{p\dot{q} - H(qp)\}\, dt = \text{extremum}. \tag{33}$$

Let us imagine the Fourier expansion of L inserted in this and take the interval of time $t_1 - t_0$ sufficiently large; then only the constant term in L will make a contribution to the integral. The form that the principle of least action thereby acquires easily leads to the following transition to quantum mechanics:

The diagonal sum $D(L) = \sum_k L(kk)$ *will be made an extremum*:

$$D(\boldsymbol{L}) = D(\boldsymbol{p}\dot{\boldsymbol{q}} - \boldsymbol{H}(\boldsymbol{p}, \boldsymbol{q})) = \text{extremum}, \tag{34}$$

by a suitable choice of $\boldsymbol{p}$ *and* $\boldsymbol{q}$ *with fixed* $\nu(nm)$.

Thus, by putting the derivatives of $D(\boldsymbol{L})$ with respect to the elements of $\boldsymbol{p}$ and $\boldsymbol{q}$ equal to zero, we obtain the equations of motion

$$2\pi i\nu(nm)\, q(nm) = \frac{\partial D(\boldsymbol{H})}{\partial p(mn)},$$

$$2\pi i\nu(mn)\, p(mn) = \frac{\partial D(\boldsymbol{H})}{\partial q(mn)}.$$

According to (26), (31), and (16), we know that these equations of motion can be written generally in the canonical form

$$\left.\begin{aligned} \dot{\boldsymbol{q}} &= \frac{\partial \boldsymbol{H}}{\partial \boldsymbol{p}}, \\ \dot{\boldsymbol{p}} &= -\frac{\partial \boldsymbol{H}}{\partial \boldsymbol{q}}. \end{aligned}\right\} \tag{35}$$

As quantum condition, Heisenberg uses a relation established by Thomas† and Kuhn.‡ The equation

$$J = \oint p\, dq = \int_0^{1/\nu} p\dot{q}\, dt$$

of the "classical" quantum theory can, when the Fourier expansions of p and q

$$p = \sum_{\tau=-\infty}^{\infty} p_\tau e^{2\pi i\nu\tau t}, \qquad q = \sum_{\tau=-\infty}^{\infty} q_\tau e^{2\pi i\nu\tau t},$$

are introduced in, be transformed into

$$1 = 2\pi i \sum_{\tau=-\infty}^{\infty} \tau \frac{\partial}{\partial J}(q_\tau p_{-\tau}). \tag{36}$$

If, under these conditions, $p = m\dot{q}$, the p_τ can be expressed by the q_τ and in this way we obtain that classical equation the transformation of which by correspondence into a differential equation gives Thomas and Kuhn's relation. Since the presupposition $\boldsymbol{p} = m\dot{\boldsymbol{q}}$ will not be made here, we must convert Equation (36) directly into a differential equation. The sum

$$\sum_{\tau=-\infty}^{\infty} \tau \frac{\partial}{\partial J}(q_\tau p_{-\tau})$$

must correspond with

$$\frac{1}{h} \sum_{\tau=-\infty}^{\infty} (q(n+\tau, n)\, p(n, n+\tau) - q(n, n-\tau)\, p(n-\tau, n));$$

on the right-hand side of which those $q(nm)$, $p(nm)$ that have a negative index are to be put equal to zero. In this way we obtain as the transformation of (36) by correspondence the quantum condition

$$\sum_k (p(nk)\, q(kn) - q(nk)\, p(kn)) = \frac{h}{2\pi i}. \tag{37}$$

† W. Thomas, *Naturw.* **13**, 627, 1925.
‡ W. Kuhn, *Zs. f. Phys.* **33**, 408, 1925.

There is an infinite number of equations, namely one for each n. For $\boldsymbol{p} = m\dot{\boldsymbol{q}}$ this gives, in particular

$$\sum_k \nu(kn)\,|q(nk)|^2 = \frac{h}{8\pi^2 m},$$

which, as can easily be established, agrees with Heisenberg's form of the quantum conditions or the Thomas–Kuhn equation. (37) must be regarded as the appropriate generalization of this equation.

Moreover, it can be seen from (37) that the diagonal sum $D(\boldsymbol{pq})$ necessarily becomes infinite, for otherwise from (10) it would follow that $D(\boldsymbol{pq}) - D(\boldsymbol{qp}) = 0$, while (37) leads to $D(\boldsymbol{pq}) - D(\boldsymbol{qp}) = \infty$. The matrices considered are therefore never finite.†

§ 4. Consequences. Energy and Frequency Law

The statements of the preceding paragraph give the basic laws of the new mechanics completely. All other laws of quantum mechanics to which general validity is to be ascribed must be *proved* from them. The first of such laws to be proved are the *energy law* and *Bohr's frequency condition.* The energy law states that when $\boldsymbol{H}$ is the energy, $\dot{\boldsymbol{H}} = 0$, or that $\boldsymbol{H}$ is a *diagonal matrix*. The diagonal members $H(nn)$ of $\boldsymbol{H}$ are then interpreted following Heisenberg as *energies of the different states* of the system, and Bohr's frequency condition requires

$$h\nu(nm) = H(nn) - H(mm),$$

or

$$W_n = H(nn) + \text{const.}$$

Let us consider the quantities

$$\boldsymbol{d} = \boldsymbol{pq} - \boldsymbol{qp}.$$

According to (11) and (35),

$$\begin{aligned}\dot{\boldsymbol{d}} &= \dot{\boldsymbol{p}}\boldsymbol{q} + \boldsymbol{p}\dot{\boldsymbol{q}} - \dot{\boldsymbol{q}}\boldsymbol{p} - \boldsymbol{q}\dot{\boldsymbol{p}} \\ &= \boldsymbol{q}\frac{\partial \boldsymbol{H}}{\partial \boldsymbol{q}} - \frac{\partial \boldsymbol{H}}{\partial \boldsymbol{q}}\boldsymbol{q} + \boldsymbol{p}\frac{\partial \boldsymbol{H}}{\partial \boldsymbol{p}} - \frac{\partial \boldsymbol{H}}{\partial \boldsymbol{p}}\boldsymbol{p}.\end{aligned}$$

† Furthermore, they do not belong to the class of "limited" infinite matrices for a long time considered almost exclusively by mathematicians.

According to (22) and (23), therefore, $\dot{\boldsymbol{d}} = 0$ and $\boldsymbol{d}$ is a diagonal matrix. However, the diagonal members of $\boldsymbol{d}$ are determined precisely by the quantum conditions (34). Summarizing, using the unit matrix $\mathbf{1}$ defined by (6), we obtain the equation

$$\boldsymbol{pq} - \boldsymbol{qp} = \frac{h}{2\pi i}\mathbf{1}, \tag{38}$$

which we call the "refined quantum condition" and upon which all subsequent conclusions are based.

The following may be deduced from the form of this equation: if an equation (A) is derived from (38), (A) remains correct when $\boldsymbol{p}$ is interchanged with $\boldsymbol{q}$ and h is simultaneously replaced by $-h$. Consequently, of the equations

$$\boldsymbol{p}^n\boldsymbol{q} = \boldsymbol{q}\boldsymbol{p}^n + n\frac{h}{2\pi i}\boldsymbol{p}^{n-1}, \tag{39}$$

$$\boldsymbol{q}^n\boldsymbol{p} = \boldsymbol{p}\boldsymbol{q}^n - n\frac{h}{2\pi i}\boldsymbol{q}^{n-1}, \tag{39'}$$

for example, only one needs to be proved from (38), which is easily done by induction.

We shall now first prove the energy and frequency law, as stated above, for the case

$$\boldsymbol{H} = \boldsymbol{H}_1(\boldsymbol{p}) + \boldsymbol{H}_2(\boldsymbol{q}).$$

According to the statements of § 1, in this $\boldsymbol{H}_1(\boldsymbol{p})$ and $\boldsymbol{H}_2(\boldsymbol{q})$ can formally be replaced by sums of power

$$\boldsymbol{H}_1 = \sum_s a_s\boldsymbol{p}^s, \qquad \boldsymbol{H}_2 = \sum_s b_s\boldsymbol{q}^s.$$

Formulae (39) and (39′) then show that

$$\left.\begin{aligned} \boldsymbol{Hq} - \boldsymbol{pH} &= \frac{h}{2\pi i}\frac{\partial \boldsymbol{H}}{\partial \boldsymbol{p}}, \\ \boldsymbol{Hp} - \boldsymbol{pH} &= -\frac{h}{2\pi i}\frac{\partial \boldsymbol{H}}{\partial \boldsymbol{q}} \end{aligned}\right\} \tag{40}$$

and comparison with the equations of motion (35) gives

$$\left.\begin{aligned}\dot{\boldsymbol{q}} &= \frac{2\pi i}{h}(\boldsymbol{Hq} - \boldsymbol{qH}),\\ \dot{\boldsymbol{p}} &= \frac{2\pi i}{h}(\boldsymbol{Hp} - \boldsymbol{pH}).\end{aligned}\right\} \tag{41}$$

If, now, the matrix $\boldsymbol{Hg} - \boldsymbol{gH}$ is denoted for short by $\begin{vmatrix}\boldsymbol{H}\\ \boldsymbol{g}\end{vmatrix}$, the following relation holds

$$\begin{vmatrix}\boldsymbol{H}\\ \boldsymbol{ab}\end{vmatrix} = \begin{vmatrix}\boldsymbol{H}\\ \boldsymbol{a}\end{vmatrix}\boldsymbol{b} + \boldsymbol{a}\begin{vmatrix}\boldsymbol{H}\\ \boldsymbol{b}\end{vmatrix}; \tag{42}$$

from which, however, it can be deduced generally for $\boldsymbol{g} = \boldsymbol{g}(\boldsymbol{p}, \boldsymbol{q})$ that

$$\dot{\boldsymbol{g}} = \frac{2\pi i}{h}\begin{vmatrix}\boldsymbol{H}\\ \boldsymbol{g}\end{vmatrix} = \frac{2\pi i}{h}(\boldsymbol{Hg} - \boldsymbol{gH}) \tag{43}$$

since, for proof, we need only to calculate $\dot{\boldsymbol{g}}$ by means of (11), (11) as a function of $\boldsymbol{p}$, $\boldsymbol{q}$ and $\dot{\boldsymbol{p}}$, $\dot{\boldsymbol{q}}$, and $\begin{vmatrix}\boldsymbol{H}\\ \boldsymbol{g}\end{vmatrix}$ by means of (42) as a function of $\boldsymbol{p}$, $\boldsymbol{q}$ and $\begin{vmatrix}\boldsymbol{H}\\ \boldsymbol{p}\end{vmatrix}$, $\begin{vmatrix}\boldsymbol{H}\\ \boldsymbol{q}\end{vmatrix}$, and then imagine (41) as applied. If, in particular, we put $\boldsymbol{g} = \boldsymbol{H}$ in (43), we obtain

$$\dot{\boldsymbol{H}} = 0. \tag{44}$$

After the energy law has been proved in this way and $\boldsymbol{H}$ has been shown to be a diagonal matrix, (41) acquires the form

$$h\nu(nm)\,qn(m) = (H(nn) - H(mm))\,q(nm),$$
$$h\nu(nm)\,pn(m) = (H(nn) - H(mm))\,p(nm),$$

from which the frequency conditions follow.

If we now pass to more general Hamiltonian functions $\boldsymbol{H}^* = \boldsymbol{H}^*(\boldsymbol{pq})$, it can easily be seen from examples, such as, for instance, $\boldsymbol{H}^* = \boldsymbol{p}^2\boldsymbol{q}$, that in general $\dot{\boldsymbol{H}}^*$ is no longer equal to 0. It can be seen, however, that the Hamiltonian function $\boldsymbol{H} = \frac{1}{2}(\boldsymbol{p}^2\boldsymbol{q} + \boldsymbol{qp}^2)$ yields the same equations of motion as $\boldsymbol{H}^*$, and that $\dot{\boldsymbol{H}}$ again becomes equal to zero. Consequently, we state the energy and frequency law as follows: *For each function* $\boldsymbol{H}^* = \boldsymbol{H}^*(\boldsymbol{q}, \boldsymbol{p})$ *there is a function* $\boldsymbol{H} = \boldsymbol{H}(\boldsymbol{p}, \boldsymbol{q})$ *such that* $\boldsymbol{H}^*$ *and* $\boldsymbol{H}$ *as Hamiltonian functions yield the same equations of motion and that for these equations of motion* $\boldsymbol{H}$ *takes over the role of the time-constant energy satisfying the frequency conditions.*

According to the arguments given above, it is sufficient to show that the function $\boldsymbol{H}$ to be given satisfies not only

$$\frac{\partial \boldsymbol{H}}{\partial \boldsymbol{p}} = \frac{\partial \boldsymbol{H}^*}{\partial \boldsymbol{p}}, \qquad \frac{\partial \boldsymbol{H}}{\partial \boldsymbol{q}} = \frac{\partial \boldsymbol{H}^*}{\partial \boldsymbol{q}} \tag{45}$$

but also Equations (40). According to § 1, $\boldsymbol{H}^*$ can be represented formally as the sum of power products in $\boldsymbol{p}$ and $\boldsymbol{q}$, and because of the linearity of Equations (40) and (45) in $\boldsymbol{H}$, $\boldsymbol{H}^*$ we have simply to give for each individual summand in $\boldsymbol{H}^*$ the corresponding summand in $\boldsymbol{H}$. Consequently, we need only consider the case

$$\boldsymbol{H}^* = \prod_{j=1}^{k} (\boldsymbol{p}^{s_j} \boldsymbol{q}^{r_j}). \tag{46}$$

According to the observations of § 2, Equations (45) must be satisfied by formulating $\boldsymbol{H}$ as a linear form of those power products in $\boldsymbol{p}$, $\boldsymbol{q}$ which arise from $\boldsymbol{H}^*$ by cyclic permutations of the factors; in this process, only the sum of the coefficients must be held equal to 1. It is not so easy to answer the question of how these coefficients are to be selected and, therefore, Equations (40) are to be satisfied. It may suffice here to deal with the case $k = 1$, i.e.

$$\boldsymbol{H}^* = \boldsymbol{p}^s \boldsymbol{q}^r. \tag{47}$$

Formula (39) can be generalized to†

$$\boldsymbol{p}^m \boldsymbol{q}^n - \boldsymbol{q}^n \boldsymbol{p}^m = m \frac{h}{2\pi i} \sum_{e=0}^{n-1} \boldsymbol{q}^{n-1-l} \boldsymbol{p}^{m-1} \boldsymbol{q}^l. \tag{48}$$

† Another generalization is given by the formulae

$$\boldsymbol{p}^m \boldsymbol{q}^n = \sum_{j=0}^{m,n} j! \binom{m}{j} \binom{n}{j} \left(\frac{h}{2\pi i}\right)^j q^{n-j} p^{m-j},$$

$$\boldsymbol{q}^n \boldsymbol{p}^m = \sum_{j=0}^{m,n} j! \binom{m}{j} \binom{n}{j} \left(\frac{-h}{2\pi i}\right)^j p^{m-j} q^{n-j},$$

in which j takes on values up to the smaller of the numbers m and n.

For $n = 1$, this again becomes (39); in general (48) follows from the fact that because of (39)

$$p^m q^{n+1} - q^{n+1} p^m = (p^m q^n - q^n p^m)\, q + m \frac{h}{2\pi i} q^n p^{m+1}.$$

The interchange of p and q with a change in the sign of h gives the new formula

$$p^m q^n - q^n p^m = n \frac{h}{2\pi i} \sum_{j=0}^{m-1} p^{m-1-j} q^{n-1} p^j. \tag{48'}$$

Comparison with (48) gives

$$\frac{1}{s+1} \sum_{l=0}^{s} p^{s-l} q^r p^l = \frac{1}{r+1} \sum_{j=0}^{r} q^{r-j} p^s q^j. \tag{49}$$

We now state:

$$H = \frac{1}{s+1} \sum_{l=0}^{s} p^{s-l} q^r p^r \tag{50}$$

corresponds to H^* according to (47).

We need only prove (40), bearing in mind Formula (18′) from § 2.

Now, according to (50)

$$Hp - pH = \frac{1}{s+1} (q^r p^{s+1} - p^{s+1} q^r),$$

and according to (48) this is equivalent to the second of Equations (49).

Using (40), we obtain further,

$$Hq - qH = \frac{1}{r+1} (p^s q^{r+1} - q^{r+1} p^s),$$

which, according to (48′), is equivalent to the first of Equations (40). This completes the desired proof.

While in classical mechanics the fact that the energy is constant, $\dot{H} = 0$, can be read directly from the canonical equations, it can be seen that the energy law $\dot{\boldsymbol{H}} = 0$ of quantum mechanics is much less obvious.

How far its proof using the assumptions made is far from trivial can be recognized if, in closer relationship with the classical process of proof, we attempt to prove the constancy of $\boldsymbol{H}$ simply by calculating $\dot{\boldsymbol{H}}$. For this purpose we first have to represent $\dot{\boldsymbol{H}}$ as a function of $\boldsymbol{p}$, $\boldsymbol{q}$ and $\dot{\boldsymbol{p}}$, $\dot{\boldsymbol{q}}$ by means of (11), (11′), whereupon the values

$$-\frac{\partial \boldsymbol{H}}{\partial \boldsymbol{q}}, \quad \frac{\partial \boldsymbol{H}}{\partial \boldsymbol{p}}$$

must be introduced for $\dot{\boldsymbol{p}}$, $\dot{\boldsymbol{q}}$. This gives $\dot{\boldsymbol{H}}$ as a function of $\boldsymbol{p}$ and $\boldsymbol{q}$. Equation (38) or the formulae derived from it permit this function to be calculated as a sum of terms $a\boldsymbol{p}^s\boldsymbol{q}^\tau$, and it has to be shown that the coefficient a of each term disappears. This calculation is so extremely complicated† for the most general case, treated above in a different manner, that it appears hardly capable of being carried out. If, nevertheless, the energy and frequency law in such a general scope could be proved, it appears to us to offer marked support for the hope that this theory actually comprises deep physical laws.

In conclusion, we may record here a result that can easily be derived from the formulae of this section: *Equations (35) and (37) can be replaced by (38) and (44) (where* $\boldsymbol{H}$ *denotes the energy); under these conditions the frequencies can be determined from the frequency conditions.*

We shall go into the important applications that this law permits in the continuation of this paper.

. . . . .

§ 5. Harmonic Oscillator

The starting point of our treatment of an anharmonic oscillator (with an extra term $\frac{1}{3}\lambda \boldsymbol{q}^3$ in $\boldsymbol{H}$) is the theory of the harmonic oscillator; for small values of λ, the motion can be

† For the case $\boldsymbol{H} = \frac{1}{2m}\boldsymbol{p}^2 + U(\boldsymbol{q})$, it can be carried out directly by means of (39′).

regarded in accordance with Equation (51) as a perturbation of the harmonic vibration with the energy

$$\boldsymbol{H} = \frac{1}{2}\boldsymbol{p}^2 + \frac{\omega_0^2}{2}\boldsymbol{q}^2. \tag{52}$$

Even with this simple problem an extension of Heisenberg's arguments is necessary. This derives from a consideration of correspondence a fundamental statement on the form of the solution; since, in fact, classically only *one* harmonic component is present, Heisenberg formulates a matrix which represents only transitions between neighbouring states and therefore has the form

$$\boldsymbol{q} = \begin{pmatrix} 0 & q^{(01)} & 0 & 0 & 0\cdots \\ q^{(10)} & 0 & q^{(12)} & 0 & 0\cdots \\ 0 & q^{(21)} & 0 & q^{(23)} & 0\cdots \\ \cdots & \cdots & \cdots & \cdots & \cdots \end{pmatrix}. \tag{53}$$

Our endeavour is to construct the whole theory independently, without bringing in assistance from the classical theory on the basis of the correspondence principle. Consequently, we shall investigate whether the form (53) of the matrix can be derived from the basic equations themselves or, if this is not the case, what additional requirements must be set.

It can be seen directly from what was said in § 3 on the invariance with respect to permutations of rows and colums that the exact form of the matrix (53) can never be deduced from the basic equations, since if the rows and columns are permuted in the same way the canonical equations and the quantum conditions remain invariant; consequently a new and apparently different solution has been found. However, all these solutions are naturally only different with respect to the way in which they are written, i.e. the enumeration of the elements. We shall show that by a simple renumbering of the elements the solution can always be brought into the form (53). The equation of motion

$$\ddot{\boldsymbol{q}} + \omega_0^2\boldsymbol{q} = 0 \tag{54}$$

is for the elements:

$$(\nu^2(nm) - \nu_0^2)\, q(nm) = 0, \tag{55}$$

where

$$\omega_0 = 2\pi\nu_0, \qquad h\nu(nm) = W_n - W_m.$$

It follows from the refined quantum conditions

$$\boldsymbol{pq} - \boldsymbol{qp} = \frac{h}{2\pi i}\,\mathbf{1} \tag{56}$$

that for each n there must exist an n' such that $q(nn') \neq 0$; for if there were an n for which all $q(nn') = 0$, the n-th diagonal member of $\boldsymbol{pq} - \boldsymbol{qp}$ would be equal to zero, which contradicts the quantum condition. Consequently, (55) shows that an n' always exists for which

$$|W_n - W_{n'}| = h\nu_0.$$

Since, however, we have assumed in our basic principles that $W_n \neq W_m$ is always the case for $n \neq m$, not more than *two* such indices, n' and n'', can exist, for the corresponding $W_{n'}$, $W_{n''}$ are solutions of the quadratic equation

$$(W_n - x)^2 = h^2\nu_0^2;$$

if *two* such indices n', n'' actually exist, it follows for the corresponding frequencies that

$$\nu(nn') = -\nu(nn''). \tag{57}$$

Now, from (56)

$$\sum_k \nu(kn)\,|q(nk)|^2 = \nu(n'n)\,\{|q(nn')|^2 - |q(nn'')|^2\} = \frac{h}{8\pi^2}, \tag{58}$$

and the energy (52) becomes

$$H(nm) = \tfrac{1}{2}4\pi^2 \sum_k \{-\nu(nk)\,\nu(km)\,q(nk)\,q(km) + \nu_0^2 q(nk)\,q(km)\}$$

$$= 2\pi^2 \sum_k q(nk)\,q(km)\,\{\nu_0^2 - \nu(nk)\,\nu(km)\}.$$

In particular, the following relation holds for $m = n$:

$$H(nn) = W_n = 4\pi^2\nu_0^2(|q(nn')|^2 + |q(nn'')|^2). \tag{59}$$

Three cases are now possible:

(a) There is no n'' and $W_{n'} > W_n$;
(b) There is no n'' and $W_{n'} < W_n$;
(c) n'' exists.

In case (b) instead of n let us now consider n'; this corresponds to not more than two indices $(n')'$ and $(n')''$, and of these one must be equal to n. Consequently, we come back to either case (a) or case (c) and consequently can disregard (b).

In case (a), $\nu(n'n) = +\nu_0$, and it follows from (58) that:

$$\nu_0 \cdot |q(nn')|^2 = \frac{h}{8\pi^2}, \tag{60}$$

and therefore according to (59):

$$W_n = H(nn) = 4\pi^2\nu_0^2|q(nn')|^2 = \tfrac{1}{2}\nu_0 h.$$

Because of the assumption $W_n \neq W_m$ for $n \neq m$ there is at the most *one* index $n = n_0$ for case (a).

If such an n_0 exists, we can give a series or integers

$$n_0 n_1 n_2 n_3 \ldots$$

such that

$$(n_k)' = n_{k+1} \quad \text{and} \quad W_{k+1} > W_k.$$

Then in each case

$$(n_{k+1})'' = n_k.$$

Consequently, for $k > 0$, from (58) and (59):

$$H(n_k n_k) = 4\pi^2\nu_0^2\{|q(n_k, n_{k+1})|^2 + |q(n_k, n_{k-1})|^2\}, \tag{61}$$

$$\tfrac{1}{2}h = 4\pi^2\nu_0\{|q(n_k, n_{k+1})|^2 - |q(n_k, n_{k-1})|^2\}. \tag{62}$$

From (60) and (62), it follows that

$$|q(n_k, n_{k+1})|^2 = \frac{h}{8\pi^2\nu_0}(k+1), \tag{63}$$

and then from (61)

$$W_{n_k} = H(n_k, n_k) = \nu_0 h(k + \tfrac{1}{2}). \tag{64}$$

We shall now see whether it is possible that there is no n for which case (a) holds. We can then, starting with any n_0, put $n_0' = n_1$ and $n_0'' = n_1$; for each of these, again, $n_1' = n_2$, $n_1'' = n_0$, and $n_{-1}' = n_0$, $n_{-1}'' = n_{-2}$, and so on. In this way, we obtain a series of integers

$$\ldots n_{-2} n_{-1} n_0 n_1 n_2 \ldots \tag{65}$$

and Equations (61) and (62) hold for each k between $-\infty$ and $+\infty$. However, this is impossible, since according to (62) the quantities $x_k = |q(n_{k+1}, n_k)|^2$ form an equidistant series of numbers and since they are positive there must be a smallest one. We can again denote the corresponding index by n_0 and therefore come back to the previous case; consequently, Formulae (63) and (64) hold again here.

It can also be seen that each number n must be included among the numbers n_k, for otherwise, with n as the starting point we could build a new series (65) with Formula (60) holding again. Consequently, the initial members of both series have the value $W_n = H(nn)$, which is impossible.

This proves that the indices 0, 1, 2, 3 . . . can be rearranged into a new sequence $n_0, n_1, n_2, n_3 \ldots$ in such a way that Formulae (63) and (64) apply; in these new indices the solution then has Heisenberg's form (53). This therefore appears as the "normal form" of the general solution. According to (64) it has the property that

$$W_{n_{k+1}} > W_{n_k}\,.$$

If, conversely, we require that $W_n = H(nn)$ always increases with n, then necessarily $n_k = k$; this principle therefore also establishes the normal form unambiguously. But this only fixes the method of writing it and makes the calculation simpler; *physically* it gives nothing new.

This involves a deeper difference from the previously customary semi-classical determination of the stationary states. The orbits calculated classically follow one another continuously, so that in the subsequently specially selected quantum orbits a definite sequence is present *a priori.* The new mechanics shows itself as a true discontinuum theory in that here there is no question of such a sequence of quantum states defined by the physical process but the quantum numbers are in fact nothing other than distinguishing indices which can be arranged and normalized according to any practical point of view whatever (e.g. according to increasing energies W_n).

. . . . . .

PAPER 8

Quantum Mechanics of Collision Processes†‡

M. BORN

Schrödinger's form of quantum mechanics permits the frequency of a state to be defined in a natural manner with the aid of the intensity of the assigned eigenvibration. This conception leads to a theory of collision processes in which the transition probabilities are determined by the asymptotic behaviour of aperiodic solutions.

Introduction

Collision processes have not only given the most convincing experimental proof of the basic assumptions of the quantum theory but also appear suitable for elucidating the physical significance of the formal laws of the so-called "quantum mechanics". Indeed it appears that these always yield the correct term values of the stationary states and the correct amplitudes of the vibrations emitted during the transitions, but opinions are divided on the physical interpretation of the formulae. The matrix form of quantum mechanics founded by Heisenberg and developed by him together with Jordan and the author of this paper§ starts from the idea that an exact representation of the processes in space and time is quite impossible

† *Zeitschrift für Physik*, **38**, 803, 1926.

‡ For a preliminary communication on this subject see *Zs. f. Phys.* **37**, 863, 1926.

§ W. Heisenberg, *Zs. f. Phys.* **33**, 879, 1925; M. Born and P. Jordan, *ibid.* **34**, 858, 1925 (this volume, p. 183); M. Born, W. Heisenberg and P. Jordan, *ibid.* **35**, 557, 1926. See also P. A. M. Dirac, *Proc. Roy. Soc.* **109**, 642, 1925; **116**, 561, 1926.

and is therefore satisfied with the establishment of relations between observable quantities which can be explained as properties of motions only in the classical limiting case. On the other hand, Schrödinger† appears to ascribe to the waves, which he regards, in accordance with de Broglie's method, as the bearers of the atomic processes, a reality of the same type as light waves possess; he attempts "to construct wave groups which have relatively small dimensions in all directions" and which are obviously intended to represent the moving corpuscle directly.

Neither of these two conceptions appear satisfactory to me. I should like to attempt here to give a third interpretation and to test its utility on collision processes. In this attempt, I adhere to an observation of Einstein on the relationship of wave field and light quanta; he said, for example, that the waves are present only to show the corpuscular light quanta the way, and he spoke in the sense of a "ghost field". This determines the probability that a light quantum, the bearer of energy and momentum, takes a certain path; however, the field itself has no energy and no momentum.

It would be better to postpone putting these ideas into direct relationship with quantum mechanics until the incorporation of the electromagnetic field into the formalism is completed. With the complete analogy between a light quantum and an electron, however, we shall consider the formulation of the laws of the motion of electrons in a similar manner. And here it is obvious to regard the de Broglie–Schrödinger waves as the "ghost field" or, better, "guiding field".

I should therefore like to investigate experimentally the following idea: the guiding field, represented by a scalar function ψ of the coordinates of all the particles involved and the time, propagates in accordance with Schrödinger's differential equation. Momentum and energy, however, are transferred in the same way as if corpuscles (electrons) actually moved. The paths of

† E. Schrödinger, *Ann. d. Phys.* **79**, 361, 489, 734, 1926 (this volume pp. 94 and 106). Cf., particularly, the 2nd communication, p. 499. Also *Naturw.* **14**, 664, 1926.

these corpuscles are determined only to the extent that the laws of energy and momentum restrict them; otherwise, only a probability for a certain path is found, determined by the values of the ψ function. This could be summarized, somewhat paradoxically, perhaps as follows: the motion of the particles follows laws of probability, but the probability itself propagates in harmony with the causal law.†

If the three stages of the development of the quantum theory are reviewed, it can be seen that the earliest, that of the periodic processes, is quite unsuitable for testing the applicability of such an idea. The second stage, that of the aperiodic stationary processes, yields somewhat more, and in the present paper we shall deal with this. However, only the third stage, that of the non-stationary processes, can be truly decisive; here it must be shown whether the interference of damped "waves of probability" is adequate to explain those phenomena which apparently indicate a space-time-less coupling.

A refinement of the concepts is only possible on the basis of the mathematical development;‡ consequently, we turn to this immediately and come back to the hypothesis itself later.

§ 1. Definition of the Weights and Frequencies for Periodic Systems

We begin with a purely formal consideration of the discrete stationary states of a non-degenerate system. This may be characterized by Schrödinger's differential equation

$$[H - W, \psi] = 0. \tag{1}$$

† This means that a knowledge of the state at all points at one moment determines the distribution of the state at all later times.

‡ In the mathematical preparation of this paper, Prof. N. Wiener of Cambridge, Mass., helped me in the most friendly manner; I should like here to express my thanks for this and to acknowledge that without it I would not have achieved my purpose.

Let the eigenfunctions be normalized to 1:†

$$\int \psi_n(q)\, \psi_m^*(q)\, dq = \delta_{nm}. \tag{2}$$

Any arbitrary function $\psi(q)$ can be expanded in terms of the eigenfunctions:

$$\psi(q) = \sum_n c_n \psi_n(q). \tag{3}$$

Up to the present time, attention has been directed only to the eigenvibrations ψ_n and the eigenvalues W_n. Our conception, explained in the introduction, gives rise to the idea of bringing the transformation represented by (3) into relationship with the probability so that in an assembly of dentical, uncoupled, atoms the states occur with a definite frequency.

The completeness relation

$$\int |\psi(q)|^2\, dq = \sum_n |c_n|^2 \tag{4}$$

leads us to regard this integral as the number of atoms, since for the occurrence of a single normalized eigenvibration it has the value 1 (or: the *a priori* weights of the states are 1), $|c_n|^2$ denotes the frequency of the state n, and the total number is composed additively of these components.

In order to justify this interpretation, let us consider, for instance, the motion of a mass point in three-dimensional space under the action of the potential energy $U(x, y, z)$; then the differential equation (1) is

$$\nabla^2\psi + \frac{8\pi^2\mu}{h^2}(W - U)\,\psi = 0. \tag{5}$$

If, in this, for W and ψ we put an eigenvalue W_n and an eigenfunction ψ_n, multiply the equation by ψ_m^*, and integrate over the space ($dV = dx\, dy\, dz$), we obtain:

$$\iiint \left\{\psi_m^* \nabla^2\psi_n + \frac{8\pi^2\mu}{h^2}(W_n - U)\,\psi_n\psi_m^*\right\} dV = 0.$$

† For simplicity, I put the density function equal to 1.

According to Green's law, this gives, taking the orthogonality relations (2) into account,

$$\delta_{mn} W_n = \iiint \left\{ \frac{h^2}{8\pi^2\mu} (\text{grad}\, \psi_n \cdot \text{grad}\, \psi_m^*) + U\psi_n\psi_m^* \right\} dV. \tag{6}$$

Each energy level can therefore be regarded as a space integral of the energy density of the eigenvibrations.

If, now, for any function we form the corresponding integrals

$$W = \iiint \left\{ \frac{h^2}{8\pi^2\mu} |\text{grad}\, \psi|^2 + U|\psi|^2 \right\} dV, \tag{7}$$

by substituting the expansion (3) for it, we obtain the expression

$$W = \sum_n |c_n|^2\, W_n. \tag{8}$$

According to our interpretation of the $|c_n|^2$, the right-hand side is the mean value of the total energy of a system of atoms; this mean value can therefore be represented as a space integral of the energy density of the function ψ.

But otherwise, nothing fundamental in favour of our statement can be obtained as long as we consider periodic processes.

§ 2. Aperiodic Systems

We therefore pass to aperiodic processes and for simplicity first consider the case of uniform motion in a straight line along the x-axis. Here the differential equation is:

$$\frac{d^2\psi}{dx^2} + k^2\psi = 0, \qquad k^2 = \frac{8\pi^2\mu}{h^2} W; \tag{1}$$

it has as eigenvalues all positive values of W and as eigenfunctions

$$\psi = ce^{\pm ikx}.$$

In order to be able the define weights and frequencies here, we must first normalize the eigenfunction. The integral formula analogous to (2) fails (the integral is divergent); it is an obvious matter to use, instead of this, the "mean value":

$$\lim_{a\to\infty} \frac{1}{2a} \int_{-a}^{+a} |\psi(k, x)|^2 \, dx = \lim_{a\to\infty} \frac{c^2}{2a} \int_{-a}^{+a} c^{ikx} e^{-ikx} \, dx = 1; \qquad (2)$$

from this it follows that $c = 1$, and we have as *normalized eigenfunctions*

$$\psi(k, x) = e^{\pm ikx}. \qquad (3)$$

Each function of x can be composed of these. The k scale is still to be chosen, i.e. we must determine just in which section the weight 1 shall fall. For this purpose we consider free motion as the limiting case of a periodic motion, namely the eigenvibrations of a finite segment of the x-axis. Then, as is known, their number per unit length and per interval $(k, k + \Delta k)$ is $\frac{\Delta k}{2\pi} = \Delta\left(\frac{1}{\lambda}\right)$, where λ is the wavelength. We shall therefore put

$$\psi(x) = \int_{-\infty}^{\infty} c(k)\, \psi(k, x)\, d\frac{k}{2\pi} = \frac{1}{2\pi} \int_{-\infty}^{\infty} c(k)\, e^{ikx}\, dk \qquad (4)$$

with

$$c(-k) = c^*(k) \qquad (5)$$

and expect that $|c(k)|^2$ will then be the measure of the frequency for the interval $\frac{1}{2\pi} dk$.

For a mixture of atoms in which the eigenfunctions occur in the distribution given by $c(k)$, the number is represented analogously to § 1, (4) by the integral

$$\int_{-\infty}^{\infty} |\psi(x)|^2 \, dx = \frac{1}{(2\pi)^2} \int_{-\infty}^{\infty} dx \left| \int_{-\infty}^{\infty} c(k)\, e^{ikx}\, dk \right|^2 . \qquad (6)$$

If we take the case that only the small interval $k_1 \leqq k \leqq k_2$ is occupied,

$$\int_{-\infty}^{\infty} c(k)\, e^{ikx}\, dk = \bar{c} \int_{k_1}^{k_2} e^{ikx}\, dk = \frac{\bar{c}}{ix}\,(e^{ik_2x} - e^{ik_1x}),$$

where $\bar{c}$ denotes a mean value. Consequently we have

$$\int_{-\infty}^{\infty} |\psi(x)|^2\, dx = \frac{|\bar{c}|^2}{4\pi^2} \int_{-\infty}^{\infty} \frac{dx}{x^2}\,(e^{ik_2x} - e^{ik_1x})\,(e^{-ik_2x} - e^{-ik_1x})$$

$$= \frac{|\bar{c}|^2}{4\pi^2}\, 4 \int_{-\infty}^{\infty} \frac{dx}{x^2} \sin^2 \frac{k_2 - k_1}{2} x$$

$$= \frac{1}{2\pi} |\bar{c}|^2\, (k_2 - k_1).$$

Now, the momentum of the translational motion belonging to the eigenfunction (3) is, according to de Broglie,

$$p = \frac{h}{\lambda} = \frac{h}{2\pi} k. \tag{7}$$

It is probably not superfluous to observe that this can also be regarded as a "matrix"; then the matrices in the continuous spectrum must be defined not by integrals but by mean values, i.e. here

$$p(k, k') = \frac{h}{2\pi i} \lim_{a \to \infty} \frac{1}{2a} \int_{-a}^{+a} \psi^*(k, x) \frac{\partial \psi(k, x)}{\partial x}\, dx$$

$$= \frac{h}{2\pi i} \lim_{a \to \infty} \frac{1}{2a} \int_{-a}^{+a} e^{-ikx}\, ik' e^{ik'x}\, dx. \tag{8}$$

$$p(k, k') = \begin{cases} \dfrac{h}{2\pi} k & \text{for} \quad k = k', \\ 0 & \text{for} \quad k \neq k'. \end{cases}$$

If we now replace $\Delta k = k_2 - k_1$ by $(2\pi/h)\,\Delta p$, we have finally

$$\int_{-\infty}^{\infty} |\psi(x)|^2\, dx = |\bar{c}|^2 \frac{\Delta p}{h}. \tag{9}$$

Consequently, we have the result that a cell of the extension in length $\Delta x = 1$ and the extension in momentum $\Delta p = h$ has the weight 1, in agreement with Sackur and Tetrode's law,† which has repeatedly been confirmed by experiment, and that $|c(k^2)|^2$ is the frequency for a motion with the momentum $p = (h/2\pi)k$.

Now we pass to accelerated motions. Here, of course, we can define a definite distribution of the processes in an analogous manner. However, in the case of collision processes this is not a rational way to put the question. In these processes, any motion before and after the collision has a rectilinear asymptote. Consequently, a very long time (in comparison to the actual time of collision) before and after the collision the particles are in a practically free state. Hence in agreement with the experimental way to put the problem, we come to the following interpretation: let the distribution function $|c(k)|^2$ be known for the asymptotic motion before the collision; is it possible to calculate the distribution function after the collision from this?

Naturally, here we are dealing with a stationary stream of particles. Consequently, the mathematical problem runs as follows: the stationary vibration field ψ must be divided into incoming and outgoing waves; these are asymptotically plane waves. Now both are represented by Fourier integrals of the form (4) and the coefficient functions $c(k)$ for the incoming rays are selected arbitrarily; then it is to be shown that the $c(k)$ for the outgoing rays are completely determined. They yield the distribution into which a predetermined mixture of particles is converted by the collision.

. . . . .

† A. Sackur, *Ann. d. Phys.* **36**, 958, 1911; **40**, 67, 1913; H. Tetrode, *Phys. Zs.* **14**, 212, 1913; *Ann. d. Phys.* **38**, 434, 1912.

§ 5. Generalization to Three Degrees of Freedom. Inertial Motion

We now consider a particle moving in space under the action of the potential energy $U(x, y, z)$.

. . . . .

For this case the differential equation runs

$$\nabla^2 \psi + (k^2 - V)\psi = 0, \tag{5}$$

where we have put

$$k^2 = \frac{8\pi^2\mu}{h^2} W, \qquad V(x, y, z) = \frac{8\pi^2\mu}{h^2} U(x, y, z). \tag{6}$$

For the *inertial motion* ($V = 0$) we have the differential equation

$$\nabla^2 \psi + k^2 \psi = 0 \tag{7}$$

and the solution

$$\psi = e^{i(\boldsymbol{k} \cdot \boldsymbol{r})}; \tag{8}$$

here $\boldsymbol{r}$ is the vector x, y, z, and the vector $\boldsymbol{k}$ satisfies the equation

$$|\boldsymbol{k}|^2 = k_x^2 + k_y^2 + k_z^2 = k^2, \tag{9}$$

and is equal to the momentum vector apart from a factor

$$\boldsymbol{p} = \frac{h}{2\pi} \boldsymbol{k}. \tag{10}$$

The de Broglie wavelength is given by

$$\frac{h}{\lambda} = p = |\boldsymbol{p}| = \frac{h}{2\pi} k.$$

. . . . .

The most general solution of (7) is

$$\psi(\boldsymbol{r}) = u_0(\boldsymbol{r}) = \int c(\boldsymbol{s})\, e^{ik(\boldsymbol{r} \cdot \boldsymbol{s})}\, d\omega, \quad c(\boldsymbol{s}) = c^*(\boldsymbol{s}), \tag{11}$$

where $\boldsymbol{s}$ is a unit vector and $d\omega$ is an element of solid angle. It represents inertial motions of all possible directions with the same energy; according to our principles, $|c(\boldsymbol{s})|^2$ is the number of particles per unit solid angle that travel in the direction $\boldsymbol{s}$.

. . . . .

§ 6. Elastic Collisions

We now pass to integration of the general equation (5), § 5

$$\nabla^2\psi + (k^2 - V)\psi = 0; \tag{1}$$

physically it represents the case in which an electron collides with a non-excitable atom.

As in § 3, we determine ψ by an iteration process in which the function just introduced u_0, (11), § 5, serves as the starting point. Then we calculate $u_1, u_2, \ldots$ according to the series from the approximate equations

$$\nabla^2 u_n + k^2 u_n = V u_{n-1} = F_{n-1}. \tag{2}$$

Green's law gives the solution that corresponds to outgoing waves with the time factor e^{ikvt} in the form:

$$u_n(\boldsymbol{r}) = -\frac{1}{4\pi}\int F_{n-1}(\boldsymbol{r}')\frac{e^{-ik|\boldsymbol{r}-\boldsymbol{r}'|}}{|\boldsymbol{r}-\boldsymbol{r}'|}\,dV', \tag{3}$$

where $\boldsymbol{r}'$ denotes the vector with the components x', y', z', and $dV' = dx'\,dy'\,dz'$. The convergence of the process can be proved on the basis of the assumption that V tends to zero as r^{-2}; however, we do not go into this but assume that the series

$$\psi(\boldsymbol{r}) = \sum_{n=0}^{\infty} u_n(\boldsymbol{r})$$

represents the solution.

Let us investigate the asymptotic behaviour of $u_n(\boldsymbol{r}')$. We write

$$u_n(x, y, z) = -\frac{1}{4\pi}\iiint F_{n-1}(x'y'z')$$

$$\times \frac{e^{-ik\sqrt{(x-x')^2+(y-y')^2+(z-z')^2}}}{\sqrt{(x-x')^2+(y-y')^2+(z-z')^2}}\,dx'\,dy'\,dz'.$$

Now we again carry out the rotation of the coordinate system given in § 5 and subject the integration variables to the same rotation. Then

$$u_n(x, y, z) = u_n(a_{13}Z, a_{23}Z, a_{33}Z)$$

$$= -\frac{1}{4\pi}\iiint F_{n-1}(X', Y', Z')\,\frac{e^{-ik\sqrt{X'^2+Y'^2+(Z-Z')^2}}}{\sqrt{X'^2 + Y'^2 + (Z - Z')^2}}$$

$$\times\, dX'\, dY'\, dZ'; \qquad (4)$$

under these circumstances

$$F_{n-1}(X', Y', Z') = F_{n-1}(a_{11}X' + a_{12}Y' + a_{13}Z', \ldots). \qquad (5)$$

Now we introduce polar coordinates:

$$X' = \varrho \sin\vartheta \cos\varphi, \qquad Y' = \varrho \sin\vartheta \sin\varphi, \qquad Z' = \varrho \cos\vartheta.$$

Then

$$u_n = -\frac{1}{4\pi}\int_0^{2\pi} d\varphi \int_0^{\infty} \varrho^2\, d\varrho \int_0^{\pi} \sin\vartheta\, d\vartheta\, F_{n-1}(\varrho \sin\vartheta \cos\varphi, \ldots)$$

$$\times\, \frac{e^{-ik\sqrt{\varrho^2+Z^2-2\varrho Z\cos\vartheta}}}{\sqrt{\varrho^2 + Z^2 - 2\varrho Z \cos\vartheta}}.$$

Finally, instead of ϑ we introduce the integration variable μ by means of the relations

$$\sqrt{\varrho^2 + Z^2 - 2\varrho Z \cos\vartheta} = Z\mu,$$

$$\sin\vartheta\, d\vartheta = \frac{Z}{\varrho}\mu\, d\mu;$$

whereupon the limits of the integration become

$$\vartheta = 0:\quad \mu = \left|\frac{\varrho}{Z} - 1\right|; \qquad \vartheta = \pi:\quad \mu = \frac{\varrho}{Z} + 1$$

and $\cos\vartheta$, $\sin\vartheta$ are certain functions $c(\varrho, Z, \mu)$, $s(\varrho, Z, \mu)$, which at the lower limit assume the values $c = 1$, $s = 0$ and at the upper limit the values $c = -1$, $s = 0$. In this way we obtain

$$u_n = -\frac{1}{4\pi}\int_0^{2\pi} d\varphi \int_0^{\infty} \varrho\, d\varrho \int_{|(\varrho/Z)-1|}^{(\varrho/Z)+1} F'_{n-1}(\varrho s\cos\varphi, \varrho s\sin\varphi, \varrho c)\, e^{-ik\mu Z}\, d\mu .$$

Partial integration gives from this, as in § 5, the asymptotic form:

$$u_n^{\infty} = \frac{1}{4\pi}\int_0^{2\pi} d\varphi \int_0^{\infty} \varrho\, d\varrho \frac{1}{ikZ}$$
$$\times \{F'_{n-1}(0, 0, \varrho)\, e^{-ik(Z+\varrho)} - F'_{n-1}(0, 0, -\varrho)\, e^{-ik|Z-\varrho|}\}.$$

Here, from (5)

$$F'_{n-1}(0, 0, \varrho) = F_{n-1}(a_{13}\varrho, a_{23}\varrho, a_{33}\varrho) = F_{n-1}\left(\frac{\varrho x}{r}, \frac{\varrho y}{r}, \frac{\varrho z}{r}\right),$$
$$F'_{n-1}(0, 0, -\varrho) = F_{n-1}(-a_{13}\varrho, -a_{23}\varrho, -a_{33}\varrho)$$
$$= F_{n-1}\left(-\frac{\varrho x}{r}, -\frac{\varrho y}{r}, -\frac{\varrho z}{r}\right).$$

Thus

$$u_n^{\infty} = \frac{e^{-ikr}}{2ikr}\int_0^{\infty} \varrho\, d\varrho\, F_{n-1}\left(\frac{\varrho x}{r}, \frac{\varrho y}{r}, \frac{\varrho z}{r}\right) e^{-ik\varrho}$$
$$- \frac{e^{-ikr}}{2ikr}\int_0^{r} \varrho\, d\varrho\, F_{n-1}\left(-\frac{\varrho x}{r}, \ldots\right) e^{ik\varrho}$$
$$- \frac{e^{ikr}}{2ikr}\int_r^{\infty} \varrho\, d\varrho\, F_{n-1}\left(-\frac{\varrho x}{r}, \ldots\right) e^{-ik\varrho}.$$

Here the last integral vanishes as $r \to \infty$, for since we assume that $|V| \leqq ar^{-2}$ then, because $|u_0| \leqq br^{-1}$:

$$|F_{n-1}| \leqq \frac{A}{r^3},$$

i.e.

$$\left|\int_r^{\infty} \varrho\, d\varrho\, F_{n-1}\left(-\frac{\varrho x}{r}, \ldots\right) e^{-ik\varrho}\right| \leqq A\int_r^{\infty} \frac{d\varrho}{\varrho^2} = \frac{A}{r}.$$

Consequently, we finally obtain

$$u_n^\infty = \frac{e^{-ikr}}{2ikr}\int_0^\infty \varrho\, d\varrho$$

$$\times \left\{F_{n-1}\left(\frac{\varrho x}{r}, \ldots\right) e^{-ik\varrho} - F_{n-1}\left(-\frac{\varrho x}{r}, \ldots\right) e^{-ik\varrho}\right\}. \qquad (6)$$

However, this cannot be brought into a simpler form. Consequently, we introduce the Fourier coefficient of the function F_{n-1}:

$$f_{n-1}(\boldsymbol{k}) = \frac{1}{(2\pi)^3}\iiint F_{n-1}(\boldsymbol{r})\, e^{-i(\boldsymbol{r}\cdot\boldsymbol{k})}\, dV$$

$$= \frac{1}{(2\pi)^3}\int_0^\infty r^2\, dr \iint d\omega\, F_{n-1}(r\boldsymbol{s})\, e^{-ir(\boldsymbol{k}\cdot\boldsymbol{s})}. \qquad (7)$$

By the process already carried out twice, we determine the asymptotic value and obtain:

$$f_{n-1}^\infty(k_x, k_y, k_z)$$

$$= \frac{1}{4\pi^2 ik}\int_0^\infty r\, dr \left\{F_{n-1}\left(\frac{rk_x}{k}, \ldots\right) e^{ikr} - F_{n-1}\left(-\frac{rk_x}{k}, \ldots\right) e^{-ikr}\right\}.$$

Consequently:

$$f_{n-1}^\infty\left(-k\frac{x}{r}, -k\frac{y}{}, -k\frac{z}{r}\right)$$

$$= \frac{1}{4\pi^2 ik}\int_0^\infty \varrho\, d\varrho \left\{F_{n-1}\left(\frac{\varrho x}{r}, \ldots\right) e^{-i\varrho k} - F_{n-1}\left(-\frac{\varrho x}{r}, \ldots\right) e^{i\varrho k}\right\}; \qquad (8)$$

if we substitute this in (6), we finally obtain:

$$u_n^\infty(x, y, z) = 2\pi^2 f_{n-1}^\infty\left(-k\frac{x}{r}, -k\frac{y}{r}, -k\frac{z}{r}\right)\frac{e^{-ikr}}{r}. \qquad (9)$$

If we compare this with Formulae (11) and (18) of § 5, we see that an observer at infinity will regard the scattered radiation as plane waves with the amplitude dependent on the direction $\boldsymbol{s}$:

$$\frac{k}{2\pi} 2\pi^2 \,|f_{n-1}^{\infty}(-k\boldsymbol{s})| = k\pi |f_{n-1}^{\infty}(-k\boldsymbol{s})|$$

and therefore the probability that an electron is deflected into a solid angle element $d\omega$ with the mean direction $\boldsymbol{s}$ is:

$$\Phi \, d\omega = \pi^2 k^2 \left| \sum_{n=0}^{\infty} f_n^{\infty}(-k\boldsymbol{s}) \right|^2 d\omega. \tag{10}$$

Asymptotically, the over-all solution has the form

$$\psi^{\infty} = u_0 + \sum_{n=1}^{\infty} u_n^{\infty} = \frac{2\pi}{k} \left\{ |c(\boldsymbol{s})| \, e^{ik(r+\delta)} + k\pi \sum_{n=1}^{\infty} f_n^{\infty}(-k\boldsymbol{s}) \, e^{-ikr} \right\}.$$

If the time factor e^{ikvt} is introduced into this, Formula (4), § 5, easily gives the "conservation of the number of particles".

To a first approximation, we have

$$\Phi \, d\omega = \pi^2 k^2 |f_0^{\infty}(-k\boldsymbol{s})|^2 \, d\omega, \tag{11}$$

in which one can either calculate f_0 exactly from the formula

$$f_0(\boldsymbol{k}) = \frac{1}{(2\pi)^3} \int F_0(\boldsymbol{r}) \, e^{-i(\boldsymbol{k}\cdot\boldsymbol{r})} \, dV \tag{12}$$

or simply make use of the asymptotic expression [from (8)]

$$f_0^{\infty}(-k\boldsymbol{s}) = \frac{1}{4\pi^2 ik} \int_0^{\infty} \varrho \, d\varrho \{F_0(\varrho\boldsymbol{s}) \, e^{ik\varrho} - F_0(-\varrho\boldsymbol{s}) \, e^{-ik\varrho}\}. \tag{13}$$

§ 7. Inelastic electron collisions

Let an atom (or a molecule; we shall always speak of "atom") be given by the Hamiltonian function $H^a(p, q)$;† and let Schrödinger's differential equation for this system be solved so that we know the eigenvalues W_n^a and eigenfunctions $\psi_n^a(q)$ which

† For brevity we write p, q instead of $p_1, p_2, \ldots, p_f, q_1, \ldots, q_f$.

satisfy the equations

$$[H^a - W_n^a, \psi_n^a] = 0. \tag{1}$$

Let an electron collide with this atom; the Hamiltonian function of the free electron is

$$H^\varepsilon = \frac{1}{2\mu}(p_x^2 + p_y^2 + p_z^2),$$

the eigenvalues are all positive numbers W^ε and the eigenfunctions are

$$e^{\pm k(r \cdot s)}, \qquad k^2 = \frac{8\pi^2\mu}{h^2} W^\varepsilon; \tag{2}$$

the general solution corresponding to incoming waves is

$$\psi_k^\varepsilon = \int_{(r \cdot s)>0} c^0(s)\, e^{ik(r \cdot s)}\, d\omega; \tag{3}$$

it satisfies the differential equation

$$[H^\varepsilon - W^\varepsilon, \psi_k^\varepsilon] = 0 \quad \text{or} \quad \nabla^2\psi_k^\varepsilon + k^2\psi_k^\varepsilon = 0. \tag{4}$$

Let the potential energy between the atom and the electron be

$$U(q; x, y, z). \tag{5}$$

The interaction between the two particles leads to the Hamiltonian function:

$$H = H^0 + \lambda H^{(1)},$$

where

$$H^0 = H^a + H^\varepsilon,$$

$$\lambda H^{(1)} = U.$$

The unperturbed system has the solution

$$W_{nk}^0 = W_n^a + W^\varepsilon, \qquad \psi_{nk}^0 = \psi_n^a \psi_k^\varepsilon.$$

We solve Schrödinger's differential equation for the perturbed system

$$[H - W, \psi] = 0$$

by the formula

$$\psi = \psi^0 + \lambda\psi^{(1)} + \cdots$$

Then we obtain the approximate equations

$$[H^0 - W^0_{nk}, \psi^{(1)}_{nk}] = - U\psi^0_{nk},$$
$$[H^0 - W^0_{nk}, \psi^{(2)}_{nk}] = - U\psi^{(1)}_{nk},$$
$$\dots\dots\dots\dots\dots\dots\dots\dots$$

the left-hand sides of which coincide. We write it in detail:

$$[H^a, \psi^{(1)}_{nk}] + [H^\varepsilon, \psi^{(1)}_{nk}] - W^0_{nk}\psi^{(1)}_{nk} = - U\psi^0_{nk},$$

or

$$[H^a, \psi^{(1)}_{nk}] - \frac{h^2}{8\pi^2\mu}\nabla^2\psi^{(1)}_{nk} - W^{(0)}_{nk}\psi^{(1)}_{nk} = - U\psi^0_{nk}.$$

Let us attempt to solve this equation by the formula

$$\psi^{(1)}_{nk} = \sum_m u^{(1)}_{nm}(\boldsymbol{r})\,\psi^a_m,$$

i.e. through an expansion in terms of the eigenfunctions of the unperturbed atom alone, the coefficients of which are still undetermined functions of the position vector $\boldsymbol{r}$ of the electron.

Now, according to (1) we shall have

$$[H^a, \psi^{(1)}_{nk}] = \sum_m u^{(1)}_{nm}(\boldsymbol{r})\,[H^a, \psi^a_m]$$
$$= \sum_m u^{(1)}_{nm}(\boldsymbol{r})\,W^a_m\psi^a_m.$$

Let us expand the function given on the right-hand side in the same way:

$$U\psi^0_{nk} = \psi^\varepsilon_k \cdot U\psi^a_n = \psi^\varepsilon_k \sum_m U_{nm}\psi^a_m;$$

The coefficients form the matrix corresponding to the potential energy. If we insert this expression in the differential equation, we obtain

$$\sum_m \psi^a_m \left\{u^{(1)}_{nm}(\boldsymbol{r})\,W^a_m - \frac{h^2}{8\pi^2\mu}\nabla^2 u^{(1)}_{nm} - u^{(1)}_{nm}(W^a_n + W^\varepsilon)\right\}$$
$$= - \sum_m \psi^a_m U_{nm}\psi^\varepsilon_k.$$

By equating the coefficients of ψ^a_m, we obtain from this a differential equation for $u^{(1)}_{nm}(\boldsymbol{r})$; if we multiply this by $-\dfrac{8\pi^2\mu}{h^2}$ and write for brevity

$$V = \frac{8\pi^2\mu}{h^2} U, \qquad V_{nm} = \frac{8\pi^2\mu}{h^2} U_{nm}, \tag{6}$$

$$k_{nm}^2 = \frac{8\pi^2\mu}{h^2}(W_n^a - W_m^a + W^\varepsilon) = \frac{8\pi^2\mu}{h^2}(h\nu_{nm}^a + W^\varepsilon), \tag{7}$$

we find

$$\nabla^2 u_{nm}^{(1)} + k_{nm}^2 u_{nm}^{(1)} = V_{nm}\psi_k^\varepsilon. \tag{8}$$

Consequently, we have reduced the problem to that of the inelastic collision treated above, for all the subsequent approximations lead to the same wave equation. The difference from the previous situation is, however, as follows: each *transition* $(n \to m)$ of the atom corresponds to a particular differential equation the right-hand side of which is determined by the corresponding matrix element of the potential energy. Furthermore, in each case instead of the k-value of the incident wave another value $\boldsymbol{k}_{nm}$ appears to which the energy

$$W_{nm}^\varepsilon = \frac{h^2}{8\pi^2\mu} k_{nm}^2 = h\nu_{nm}^a + W^\varepsilon \tag{9}$$

corresponds. This immediately leads to the qualitative basic law of electron collisions: the energy of the electron after the collision is in general not equal to that before the collision but differs from it by an energy difference $h\nu_{nm}^a$ of the atom. Each collision process is associated with a probability function

$$\Phi_{nm} = \pi^2 k_{nm}^2 |f_0^\infty(-k_{nm}\mathfrak{s})|^2, \tag{10}$$

which can be calculated by means of Formulae (12) or (13), § 6.

§ 8. Physical Consequences

We shall first show that our formulae correctly represent the qualitative behaviour of atoms in collisions, i.e. the fact of the "energy thresholds" that we have always to regard as the fundamental pillars of the quantum theory and the greatest contradiction to classical mechanics.

We arrange the energy levels of the atom according to their magnitude:

$$W_0^a < W_1^a < W_2^a < \cdots$$

The index 0 therefore denotes the ground state, and

$$h\nu_{nm}^a = W_n^a - W_m^a > 0 \quad \text{for} \quad n > m.$$

Let us first consider the case in which the atom is initially in the ground state. Then all ν_{m0}^a are greater than 0, and it follows from (9), § 7, that

$$W_{0m}^\varepsilon = W^\varepsilon - h\nu_{m0}^a.$$

If, now, $W^\varepsilon < h\nu_{10}^a$, W_{0m}^ε would become negative for $m > 0$, which is impossible; consequently m must be equal to 0 and therefore

$$W_{00}^\varepsilon = W^\varepsilon.$$

Consequently, "elastic" reflection takes place with the yield Φ_{00}. If we allow W^ε to grow to the value

$$h\nu_{10}^a < W^\varepsilon < h\nu_{20}^a,$$

W_{0m}^ε becomes only positive for $m = 0$ and $m = 1$; consequently, we have either elastic reflection with the yield Φ_{00} or resonance excitation with the yield Φ_{01}.

If W^ε increases further, until $h\nu_{20}^a < W^\varepsilon < h\nu_{30}^a$, there are three cases: elastic reflection with the yield Φ_{00}, excitation of the first quantum jump with Φ_{01}, and excitation of the second quantum jump with Φ_{02}. And so on, similarly.

Now let us consider the case in which the atom is initially in the second quantum state ($n = 1$); then $\nu_{10}^a > 0$ and $\nu_{1m}^a < 0$ for $m = 2, 3, \ldots$

We therefore have

$$W_{10}^\varepsilon = W^\varepsilon + h\nu_{10}^a,$$

$$W_{11}^\varepsilon = W^\varepsilon,$$

$$W_{1m}^\varepsilon = W^\varepsilon - h\nu_{m1}^a, \quad m = 2, 3, \ldots$$

If, now, $W^\varepsilon < h\nu_{21}^a$, W_{1m}^ε is negative for $m = 2, 3, \ldots$; consequently, there is only either a collision of the second type with an increase in the energy of the electron by $h\nu_{10}^{a}$ and the yield Φ_{10} or elastic reflection with the yield Φ_{11}.

If

$$h\nu_{21}^{a} < W^{\varepsilon} < h\nu_{31}^{a},$$

these processes come to include the excitation of the state $n = 2$ with the yield Φ_{12}, as well. And so on.

In the general case, when the atom is initially in the state n, for

$$W^{\varepsilon} < h\nu_{n+1,n}^{a}$$

there are only collisions of the second type in which the atom falls to the states $0, 1, \ldots n - 1$ and gives up the energy values $h\nu_{n0}^{a}, h\nu_{n1}^{a}, \ldots h\nu_{n,n-1}^{a}$ with the yields $\Phi_{n0}, \Phi_{n1}, \ldots \Phi_{nn-1}$, and the elastic reflection Φ_{nn}. If W^{ε} increases beyond $h\nu_{n+1,n}^{a}$, excitations come in with the yields $\Phi_{n,n+1}, \Phi_{n,n+2}, \ldots \Phi_{n,m}$, if

$$h\nu_{n+1,n}^{a} < W^{\varepsilon} < h\nu_{m+1,n}^{a}.$$

. . . . .

§ 9. Closing Remarks

On the basis of the above discussions, I should like to put forward the opinion that quantum mechanics permits not only the formulation and solution of the problem of stationary states, but also that of transition processes. In these circumstances, Schrödinger's version appears to do justice to the facts in by far the easiest manner; moreover, it permits the retention of the conventional ideas of space and time in which events take place in a completely normal manner. On the other hand, the proposed theory does not correspond to the requirement of the causal determinacy of the individual event. In my preliminary communication I stressed this indeterminacy quite particularly, since it appears to me to be in best agreement with the practice of the experimenter. But it is natural for him who will not be satisfied with this to remain unconverted and to assume that there are other parameters, not given in the theory, that determine the individual event. In classical mechanics, these are the "phases" of the motion, i.e. the coordinates of the particles at a given instant. It appears to me to be *a priori* improbable that quantities corresponding to these phases can easily be introduced into the new theory, but Mr. Frenkel has told me that this may perhaps be the case. However this may be, this possibility would not alter anything relating to the practical indeterminacy of collision processes, since it is in fact impossible to give the values of the phases; it must in fact lead to the same formulae as the "phaseless" theory proposed here.

Index